SCOTT FORESMAN READING STREET
Weekly Tests
for College and Career Readiness

GRADE 5

Glenview, Illinois

Boston, Massachusetts

Chandler, Arizona

Upper Saddle River, New Jersey

ALWAYS LEARNING

PEARSON

ISBN-13: 978-0-328-79867-4
ISBN-10:   0-328-79867-3
6 7 8 9 10 V001 17 16 15

Contents

Unit 4 Adapting

Unit 5 Adventurers

Unit 6 The Unexpected

Directions: Read the following passage. Use information from the passage to answer the questions.

Red Kayak

by Priscilla Cummings

Up the creek, a couple private docks extended out into the water; then there was a long strip of riprap near a construction site. From that point on, it was just shoreline with trees and a lot of brown cell bush. I kept going, but toward the head of the creek, a marsh taken over by a patch of tall phragmites warned me of shallow water, and I turned the boat around, not wanting to run aground. I sped up and came back down the creek, closer to the opposite bank.

Still no sign of a red kayak or a yellow life jacket. All I wanted to do was open the throttle and head downriver to where the others were searching. My hands ached they were so cold. I stuffed one hand in the pocket and hit the cell phone. I pulled it out and saw that I had "1 missed call." Turning off the motor so I could hear, I speed-dialed home to see if Mom knew anything.

"Brady—hi!" she said. "Dad called. He said they found Mrs. DiAngelo."

"They did?"

"Yes. Downriver, near Spaniard's Neck."

"Is she okay?" I asked.

"She's alive," Mom said. "But just barely. They have *not* found Ben."

"They didn't?"

"No. They lost the kayak, Brady. So Ben is out there somewhere in the water in his life jacket."

"Oh, man, it's *cold* Mom—"

"I know . . . I know it's cold. Are you all right? Can you do this, Brady?"

"I'm all right. I'm fine," I assured her. "I need to keep looking!"

I ended the call and put the phone back in my pocket. We had to move really fast now. If Ben was in the water, his time was limited.

Tilly started barking as I picked up speed.

"Quiet!" I hollered.

Next

Text-Based Comprehension

Directions: Read the questions below and choose the best answer.

1. **Part A**

   Which word best describes the narrator at this point in the story?

   ○ **A.** pleased

   ○ **B.** comfortable

   ○ **C.** worried

   ○ **D.** lost

   Part B

   Which sentence from the passage best supports your answer to Part A?

   ○ **A.** "'He said they found Mrs. DiAngelo.'"

   ○ **B.** "'I know . . . I know it's cold.'"

   ○ **C.** "'I'm all right. I'm fine.'"

   ○ **D.** "'I need to keep looking!'"

COMMON CORE STATE STANDARDS

Literature 1. Quote accurately from a text when explaining what the text says explicitly and when drawing inferences from the text.

Next

Name _____

2. **Part A**

What conflict does the narrator face in this passage?

- ○ **A.** The boat is running out of gas.
- ○ **B.** He needs to find Ben quickly.
- ○ **C.** It will soon be too dark to see.
- ○ **D.** He is late joining the others.

Part B

Which sentence from the passage helped you identify this conflict?

- ○ **A.** "My hands ached they were so cold."
- ○ **B.** ". . . I speed-dialed home to see if Mom knew anything."
- ○ **C.** "Tilly started barking as I picked up speed."
- ○ **D.** "If Ben was in the water, his time was limited."

COMMON CORE STATE STANDARDS

Literature 1. Quote accurately from a text when explaining what the text says explicitly and when drawing inferences from the text. **Literature 2.** Determine a theme of a story, drama, or poem from details in the text, including how characters in a story or drama respond to challenges or how the speaker in a poem reflects upon a topic; summarize the text.

Next

3. **Part A**

After he hears the news about Mrs. DiAngelo and Ben, how does the narrator respond to the challenge?

○ **A.** He plans to start searching more quickly.

○ **B.** He plans to slowly search every inch of shoreline.

○ **C.** He plans to turn around and head for home.

○ **D.** He plans to wait for more news from the others.

Part B

Which detail best supports your answer to Part A?

○ **A.** "... I turned the boat around, not wanting to run aground."

○ **B.** "All I wanted to do was open the throttle and head downriver ..."

○ **C.** "We had to move really fast now."

○ **D.** "My hands ached they were so cold."

COMMON CORE STATE STANDARDS

Literature 1. Quote accurately from a text when explaining what the text says explicitly and when drawing inferences from the text. **Literature 2.** Determine a theme of a story, drama, or poem from details in the text, including how characters in a story or drama respond to challenges or how the speaker in a poem reflects upon a topic; summarize the text.

Next

Vocabulary

Directions: Read the questions below and choose the best answer.

4. **Part A**

Which meaning of the homograph "bank" is used in the first paragraph of the passage?

○ **A.** place for keeping or lending money

○ **B.** ground along a body of water

○ **C.** row or close arrangement of things

○ **D.** long pile or heap

Part B

Which detail from the paragraph helped you figure out the meaning of the homograph "bank"?

○ **A.** "turned around"

○ **B.** "sped up"

○ **C.** "closer to"

○ **D.** "the creek"

COMMON CORE STATE STANDARDS

Literature 4. Determine the meaning of words and phrases as they are used in a text, including figurative language such as metaphors and similes. **Language 4.a.** Use context (e.g., cause/effect relationships and comparisons in text) as a clue to the meaning of a word or phrase. **Language 5.c.** Use the relationships between particular words (e.g., synonyms, antonyms, homographs) to better understand each of the words.

Next

5. **Part A**

Based on context clues in the passage, what is the best definition of the word "phragmites"?

○ **A.** plants that grow in or near water

○ **B.** piles of loose rocks along a shore

○ **C.** large wading birds that eat fish

○ **D.** houses built on stilts over water

Part B

Which context clue helped you answer Part A?

○ **A.** "brown cell bush"

○ **B.** "head of the creek"

○ **C.** "marsh taken over"

○ **D.** "opposite bank"

COMMON CORE STATE STANDARDS

Literature 4. Determine the meaning of words and phrases as they are used in a text, including figurative language such as metaphors and similes. **Language 4.a.** Use context (e.g., cause/effect relationships and comparisons in text) as a clue to the meaning of a word or phrase.

Next

6. **Part A**

Which word is a synonym for the word "hollered" in the last sentence in the passage?

○ **A.** asked

○ **B.** whispered

○ **C.** shouted

○ **D.** sighed

Part B

Which detail in the sentence helped you choose the synonym in Part A?

○ **A.** the exclamation mark

○ **B.** the period

○ **C.** the pronoun *I*

○ **D.** the uppercase letter *Q*

COMMON CORE STATE STANDARDS

Literature 4. Determine the meaning of words and phrases as they are used in a text, including figurative language such as metaphors and similes. **Language 5.c.** Use the relationships between particular words (e.g., synonyms, antonyms, homographs) to better understand each of the words.

Next

Writing – Constructed Response

Based on the information in the passage from the selection *Red Kayak,* write a short description of what the narrator, Brady, is like. Think about what his words and actions tell you about him.

Introduce the topic and then develop it using details from the text. Conclude with a sentence that sums up the description. Be sure to check your writing for correct capitalization, punctuation, and spelling and correct any errors in grammar.

_____

_____

_____

_____

_____

_____

_____

_____

_____

_____

_____

_____

To the Teacher: Use the Writing Rubric on page T17 to assess students' writing.

COMMON CORE STATE STANDARDS

Writing 2. Write informative/explanatory texts to examine a topic and convey ideas and information clearly. **Writing 2.a.** Introduce a topic clearly, provide a general observation and focus, and group related information logically; include formatting (e.g., headings), illustrations, and multimedia when useful to aiding comprehension. **Writing 2.b.** Develop the topic with facts, definitions, concrete details, quotations, or other information and examples related to the topic. **Writing 2.e.** Provide a concluding statement or section related to the information or explanation presented. **Language 1.** Demonstrate command of the conventions of standard English grammar and usage when writing or speaking. **Language 2.** Demonstrate command of the conventions of standard English capitalization, punctuation, and spelling when writing.

Next

Name _____

_____

_____

_____

_____

_____

_____

_____

_____

_____

_____

_____

_____

_____

_____

_____

_____

_____

_____

_____

_____

Next

Writing – Extended Response

You have read two texts about how people deal with emergency situations.

- *Red Kayak*
- "What Will I Do in an Emergency?"

Imagine that Brady calls 9-1-1 after he finds Ben, and you are the dispatcher who answers his call. Write a dialogue between you and Brady. Use details from both texts to establish the situation, organize an event sequence, and show the responses of the characters. Remember to check your writing for correct grammar, capitalization, punctuation, and spelling.

To the Teacher: Tell students they may use the space on this page to plan their writing. Then have them write their response on the following pages. Use the Writing Rubric on page T18 to assess students' writing.

COMMON CORE STATE STANDARDS

Writing 3. Write narratives to develop real or imagined experiences or events using effective technique, descriptive details, and clear event sequence. **Writing 3.a.** Orient the reader by establishing a situation and introducing a narrator and/or characters; organize an event sequence that unfolds naturally. **Writing 3.b.** Use narrative techniques, such as dialogue, description, and pacing, to develop experiences and events or show the responses of characters to situations. **Writing 4.** Produce clear and coherent writing in which the development and organization are appropriate to task, purpose, and audience. **Language 1.** Demonstrate command of the conventions of standard English grammar and usage when writing or speaking. **Language 2.** Demonstrate command of the conventions of standard English capitalization, punctuation, and spelling when writing.

Next

Name _____

_____

_____

_____

_____

_____

_____

_____

_____

_____

_____

_____

_____

_____

_____

_____

_____

_____

_____

_____

_____

_____

Next

Directions: Read the following passage. Use information from the passage to answer the questions.

Thunder Rose

by Jerdine Nolen

Rose performed an eye-catching wonder, the likes of which was something to see. Running lightning-fast toward the herd, using Cole for support, Rose vaulted into the air and landed on the back of the biggest lead steer like he was a merry-go-round pony. Grabbing a horn in each hand, Rose twisted that varmint to a complete halt. It was just enough to restrain that top bull and the rest of the herd.

But I believe what touched that critter's heart was when Rose began humming her little tune. That cantankerous ton of beef was restless no more. He became as playful as a kitten and even tried to purr. Rose named him Tater on account of that was his favorite vegetable. Hearing Rose's little lullaby put that considerable creature to sleep was the sweetest thing I had witnessed in a long, long time.

After the dust had settled, Ma and Pa counted twenty-seven hundred head of cattle, after they added in the five hundred they already had. Using the scrap iron, Rose had to add a new section to the bull pen to hold them all.

"What did you do to the wire, Rose?" Ma asked, surprised and pleased at her daughter's latest creation.

"Oh, that," she said. "While I was staking the fence, Pa asked me to keep little Barbara Jay company. That little twisty pattern seemed to make the baby laugh. So I like to think of it as Barbara's Wire."

"That was right clever of you to be so entertaining to the little one like that!" her ma said. Rose just blushed. Over the years, that twisty wire caught on, and folks just called it barbed wire. . . .

On Rose's first trip to Abilene, while right outside of Caldwell, that irascible, full-of-outrage-and-ire outlaw Jesse Baines and his gang of desperadoes tried to rustle that herd away from Rose.

Using the spare metal rods she always carried with her, Rose lassoed those hot-tempered hooligans up good and tight. She dropped them all off to jail, tied up in a nice neat iron bow. "It wasn't any trouble at all," she told Sheriff Weaver. "Somebody had to put a stop to their thieving ways."

Next

But that wasn't the only thieving going on. The mighty sun was draining the moisture out of every living thing it touched. Even the rocks were crying out. Those clouds stood by and watched it all happen. They weren't even trying to be helpful.

Why, the air had turned so dry and sour, time seemed to all but stand still. And there was not a drop of water in sight. Steer will not move without water. And that was making these bulls mad, real mad. And when a bull gets angry, it's like a disease that's catching, making the rest of the herd mad, too. Tater was looking parched and mighty thirsty.

"I've got to do something about this!" Rose declared.

Stretching out several iron rods lasso-fashion, then launching Cole high into the air, Rose hoped she could get the heavens to yield forth. She caught hold of a mass of clouds and squeezed them hard, real hard, all the while humming her song. Gentle rain began to fall. But anyone looking could see there was not enough moisture to refresh two ants, let alone a herd of wild cows.

Text-Based Comprehension

Directions: Read the questions below and choose the best answer.

1. **Part A**

   What causes the bulls to get angry?

   ○ **A.** lack of water
   ○ **B.** lack of food
   ○ **C.** gang of rustlers
   ○ **D.** Rose lassoing clouds

   Part B

   Which detail from the passage supports your answer to Part A?

   ○ **A.** Rain begins to fall, but it's not enough.
   ○ **B.** Bulls won't go anywhere without water.
   ○ **C.** Rose decides she has to do something.
   ○ **D.** The rocks are crying out for water.

COMMON CORE STATE STANDARDS

Literature 1. Quote accurately from a text when explaining what the text says explicitly and when drawing inferences from the text.

2. Part A

Who is the narrator of this story?

○ **A.** the main character, Thunder Rose

○ **B.** the main character's parents, Ma and Pa

○ **C.** the main character's little sister, Barbara Jay

○ **D.** an observer who is not a story character

Part B

Which sentence did **not** help you identify the narrator in Part A?

○ **A.** "'What did you do to the wire, Rose?' Ma asked, surprised and pleased at her daughter's latest creation."

○ **B.** "But I believe what touched that critter's heart was when Rose began humming her little tune."

○ **C.** "The mighty sun was draining the moisture out of every living thing it touched."

○ **D.** "After the dust had settled, Ma and Pa counted twenty-seven hundred head of cattle, after they added in the five hundred they already had."

COMMON CORE STATE STANDARDS

Literature 1. Quote accurately from a text when explaining what the text says explicitly and when drawing inferences from the text. **Literature 6.** Describe how a narrator's or speaker's point of view influences how events are described.

Next

3. **Part A**

Which inference can you draw about Rose based on the passage?

○ **A.** Rose dislikes animals.

○ **B.** Rose is unhelpful.

○ **C.** Rose is fearless.

○ **D.** Rose ignores her family.

Part B

Which detail from the passage supports this inference?

○ **A.** Rose can't get enough rain from the clouds.

○ **B.** Rose entertains little Barbara Jay.

○ **C.** Rose hums her little tune to Tater.

○ **D.** Rose stops a stampeding herd.

COMMON CORE STATE STANDARDS

Literature 1. Quote accurately from a text when explaining what the text says explicitly and when drawing inferences from the text.

Next

Unit 1 • Week 2
Weekly Test

Vocabulary

Directions: Read the questions below and choose the best answer.

4. **Part A**

   Which meaning of the homonym "head" is used in the following sentence?

   "After the dust had settled, Ma and Pa counted twenty-seven hundred head of cattle, after they added in the five hundred they already had."

   ○ **A.** source of a river or stream
   ○ **B.** top or front of anything
   ○ **C.** chief person or leader
   ○ **D.** ones or individuals

   Part B

   Which detail from the sentence did **not** help you figure out the meaning of the homonym?

   ○ **A.** "counted"
   ○ **B.** "Ma and Pa"
   ○ **C.** "of cattle"
   ○ **D.** "twenty-seven hundred"

COMMON CORE STATE STANDARDS

Literature 4. Determine the meaning of words and phrases as they are used in a text, including figurative language such as metaphors and similes. **Language 4.a.** Use context (e.g., cause/effect relationships and comparisons in text) as a clue to the meaning of a word or phrase. **Language 5.c.** Use the relationships between particular words (e.g., synonyms, antonyms, homographs) to better understand each of the words.

Name _____

5. **Part A**

This sentence from the passage contains a simile: "He became as playful as a kitten and even tried to purr." What does the simile mean?

○ **A.** He began to play with a kitten.

○ **B.** He began to play like a kitten plays.

○ **C.** He began to purr like a kitten purrs.

○ **D.** He began to chase a toy mouse.

Part B

Which detail helped you figure out the meaning of the simile?

○ **A.** Rose's tune makes the mean bull nice.

○ **B.** Rose's tune makes the nice bull mean.

○ **C.** Rose jumps on the bull and rides him.

○ **D.** Rose plays with the bull like a kitten.

COMMON CORE STATE STANDARDS

Literature 4. Determine the meaning of words and phrases as they are used in a text, including figurative language such as metaphors and similes. **Language 5.a.** Interpret figurative language, including similes and metaphors, in context.

Next

6. **Part A**

Based on context clues, what does the word "considerable" mean?

- ○ **A.** plenty
- ○ **B.** careful
- ○ **C.** large
- ○ **D.** polite

Part B

Which context clue from the passage helped you answer Part A?

- ○ **A.** "restless no more"
- ○ **B.** "playful as a kitten"
- ○ **C.** "his favorite vegetable"
- ○ **D.** "ton of beef"

COMMON CORE STATE STANDARDS

Literature 4. Determine the meaning of words and phrases as they are used in a text, including figurative language such as metaphors and similes. **Language 4.a.** Use context (e.g., cause/effect relationships and comparisons in text) as a clue to the meaning of a word or phrase.

Next

Name _____

Writing – Constructed Response

Based on the information in the passage from the selection *Thunder Rose,* write a paragraph that explains what Rose did to help people. Think about Rose's actions and tell how they affected the people and animals in her life.

Introduce the topic and then develop it using details from the text. Conclude with a sentence that sums up your main point. When you have finished, read your paragraph carefully and correct any errors in grammar, capitalization, punctuation, and spelling.

_____

_____

_____

_____

_____

_____

_____

_____

_____

_____

To the Teacher: Use the Writing Rubric on page T17 to assess students' writing.

COMMON CORE STATE STANDARDS

Literature 1. Quote accurately from a text when explaining what the text says explicitly and when drawing inferences from the text. **Writing 2.** Write informative/explanatory texts to examine a topic and convey ideas and information clearly. **Writing 2.a.** Introduce a topic clearly, provide a general observation and focus, and group related information logically; include formatting (e.g., headings), illustrations, and multimedia when useful to aiding comprehension. **Writing 2.b.** Develop the topic with facts, definitions, concrete details, quotations, or other information and examples related to the topic. **Writing 4.** Produce clear and coherent writing in which the development and organization are appropriate to task, purpose, and audience. **Language 1.** Demonstrate command of the conventions of standard English grammar and usage when writing or speaking. **Language 2.** Demonstrate command of the conventions of standard English capitalization, punctuation, and spelling when writing.

Next

Writing – Extended Response

You have read two texts about courageous, resourceful young people.

- *Thunder Rose*
- *Red Kayak*

Think about the two main characters in the texts, Rose in *Thunder Rose* and Brady in *Red Kayak*. Which character do you think is braver? Why? Write an opinion piece in which you answer these questions. State your opinion and offer reasons supported by details from the selections. As you compare your ideas, use transition words such as *however, in contrast, for this reason,* and *therefore.* Provide a concluding sentence that restates your opinion. Remember to follow the conventions of standard English grammar and to use correct capitalization, punctuation, and spelling.

To the Teacher: Tell students they may use the space on this page to plan their writing. Then have them write their response on the following pages. Use the Writing Rubric on page T18 to assess students' writing.

COMMON CORE STATE STANDARDS

Literature 1. Quote accurately from a text when explaining what the text says explicitly and when drawing inferences from the text. **Writing 1.** Write opinion pieces on topics or texts, supporting a point of view with reasons and information. **Writing 1.a.** Introduce a topic or text clearly, state an opinion, and create an organizational structure in which ideas are logically grouped to support the writer's purpose. **Writing 1.b.** Provide logically ordered reasons that are supported by facts and details. **Writing 1.c.** Link opinion and reasons using words, phrases, and clauses (e.g., *consequently, specifically*). **Writing 4.** Produce clear and coherent writing in which the development and organization are appropriate to task, purpose, and audience. **Writing 9.** Draw evidence from literary or informational texts to support analysis, reflection, and research. **Language 1.** Demonstrate command of the conventions of standard English grammar and usage when writing or speaking. **Language 2.** Demonstrate command of the conventions of standard English capitalization, punctuation, and spelling when writing.

Name _____

_____

_____

_____

_____

_____

_____

_____

_____

_____

_____

_____

_____

_____

_____

_____

_____

_____

_____

_____

_____

Next

Stop

Directions: Read the following passage. Use information from the passage to answer the questions.

Island of the Blue Dolphins
by Scott O'Dell

The Island of the Blue Dolphins was my home; I had no other. It would be my home until the white men returned in their ship. But even if they came soon, before next summer, I could not live without a roof or a place to store my food. I would have to build a house. But where?

That night I slept on the rock, and the next day I began the search. The morning was clear, but to the north, banks of clouds hung low. Before long they would move in across the island, and behind them many other storms were waiting. I had no time to waste.

I needed a place that was sheltered from the wind, not too far from Coral Cove, and close to a good spring. There were two such places on the island—one on the headland and the other less than a league to the west. The headland seemed to be the more favorable of the two, but since I had not been to the other for a long time, I decided to go there and make certain.

The first thing I found, which I had forgotten, was that this place was near the wild dogs' lair. As soon as I drew near to it the leader came to the opening of the cave and watched me with his yellow eyes. If I built a hut there I would have to kill him and his pack. I planned to do this anyway, but it would take much time.

The spring was better than the one near the headland, being less brackish and having a steadier flow of water. Besides it was much easier to reach, since it came from the side of a hill and not from a ravine as the other one did. It was also close to the cliff and a ridge of rocks which would shelter my house.

The rocks were not so high as those on the headland and therefore would give me less protection from the wind, yet they were high enough, and from them I could see the north coast and Coral Cove.

The thing that made me decide on the place to build my house was the sea elephants.

The cliffs here fell away easily to a wide shelf that was partly covered when the tide came in. It was a good place for sea elephants because they could crawl halfway up the cliff if the day were stormy. On fair days they could fish among the pools or lie on the rocks. . . .

Next

On this morning the tide was low and most of the animals were far out, just hundreds of specks against the waves, yet the noise they made was deafening. I stayed there the rest of the day, looking around, and that night. At dawn when the clamor started again I left and went back to the headland.

There was another place to the south where I could have built my house, near the destroyed village of Ghalas-at, but I did not want to go there because it would remind me of the people who were gone. Also the wind blew strong in this place, blowing against the dunes which cover the middle part of the island so that most of the time sand is moving everywhere.

Next

Name _____

Text-Based Comprehension

Directions: Read the questions below and choose the best answer.

1. **Part A**

   The narrator compares several places when deciding where to build her house. Which place does she finally choose?

   ○ **A.** near the village of Ghalas-at
   ○ **B.** on the headland
   ○ **C.** on the beach
   ○ **D.** near the wild dogs' lair

   Part B

   In which sentence from the passage does the narrator reveal that choice?

   ○ **A.** "I needed a place that was sheltered from the wind, not too far from Coral Cove, and close to a good spring."
   ○ **B.** "The first thing I found, which I had forgotten, was that this place was near the wild dogs' lair."
   ○ **C.** "At dawn when the clamor started again I left and went back to the headland."
   ○ **D.** "Also the wind blew strong in this place, blowing against the dunes which cover the middle part of the island . . ."

COMMON CORE STATE STANDARDS

Literature 1. Quote accurately from a text when explaining what the text says explicitly and when drawing inferences from the text. **Literature 3.** Compare and contrast two or more characters, settings, or events in a story or drama, drawing on specific details in the text (e.g., how characters interact).

Next

2. **Part A**

How does the narrator respond to the challenge of finding a place to build a house?

- ○ **A.** She is determined and cautious.
- ○ **B.** She is lazy and careless.
- ○ **C.** She is fearful and hesitant.
- ○ **D.** She is eager and reckless.

Part B

Which sentence from the passage does **not** support your answer to Part A?

- ○ **A.** "If I built a hut there I would have to kill him and his pack."
- ○ **B.** "I stayed there the rest of the day, looking around, and that night."
- ○ **C.** ". . . since I had not been to the other [place] for a long time, I decided to go there and make certain."
- ○ **D.** "The cliffs here fell away easily to a wide shelf that was partly covered when the tide came in."

COMMON CORE STATE STANDARDS

Literature 1. Quote accurately from a text when explaining what the text says explicitly and when drawing inferences from the text. **Literature 2.** Determine a theme of a story, drama, or poem from details in the text, including how characters in a story or drama respond to challenges or how the speaker in a poem reflects upon a topic; summarize the text.

Next

3. **Part A**

What factor proved to be most important to the narrator in choosing a place for her house?

○ **A.** a source of drinking water

○ **B.** a degree of peace and quiet

○ **C.** protection from the wind

○ **D.** closeness to Coral Cove

Part B

Which sentence from the passage best supports your answer to Part A?

○ **A.** "The spring was better than the one near the headland, . . ."

○ **B.** ". . . from [the rocks] I could see the north coast and Coral Cove."

○ **C.** ". . . yet the noise [the sea elephants] made was deafening."

○ **D.** "The rocks . . . would give me less protection from the wind, . . ."

COMMON CORE STATE STANDARDS

Literature 1. Quote accurately from a text when explaining what the text says explicitly and when drawing inferences from the text.

Vocabulary

Directions: Read the questions below and choose the best answer.

4. **Part A**

   Based on context clues, what does the word "lair" mean in the following sentence?

   "The first thing I found, which I had forgotten, was that this place was near the wild dogs' lair."

   ○ **A.** sly, nasty glance
   ○ **B.** rough, rocky shoreline
   ○ **C.** supply of food
   ○ **D.** den of a wild animal

   Part B

   Which context clue from the passage helped you answer Part A?

   ○ **A.** "the leader"
   ○ **B.** "yellow eyes"
   ○ **C.** "the cave"
   ○ **D.** "a hut"

COMMON CORE STATE STANDARDS

Literature 4. Determine the meaning of words and phrases as they are used in a text, including figurative language such as metaphors and similes. **Language 4.a.** Use context (e.g., cause/effect relationships and comparisons in text) as a clue to the meaning of a word or phrase.

Next

5. **Part A**

Which meaning of the homograph "spring" is used in the following sentence?

"The spring was better than the one near the headland, being less brackish and having a steadier flow of water."

○ **A.** season between winter and summer

○ **B.** small natural stream

○ **C.** a leap or jump

○ **D.** metal coil

Part B

Which phrase from the passage is the best clue to the meaning of the homograph?

○ **A.** "near the headland"

○ **B.** "side of a hill"

○ **C.** "from a ravine"

○ **D.** "flow of water"

COMMON CORE STATE STANDARDS

Literature 4. Determine the meaning of words and phrases as they are used in a text, including figurative language such as metaphors and similes. **Language 4.a.** Use context (e.g., cause/effect relationships and comparisons in text) as a clue to the meaning of a word or phrase. **Language 5.c.** Use the relationships between particular words (e.g., synonyms, antonyms, homographs) to better understand each of the words.

Next

6. **Part A**

Which word is a synonym for the word "clamor" in the following sentence?

"At dawn when the clamor started again I left and went back to the headland."

- ○ **A.** uproar
- ○ **B.** odor
- ○ **C.** feeding
- ○ **D.** interaction

Part B

Which word from the passage helped you choose the synonym in Part A?

- ○ **A.** animals
- ○ **B.** hundreds
- ○ **C.** noise
- ○ **D.** dawn

COMMON CORE STATE STANDARDS

Literature 4. Determine the meaning of words and phrases as they are used in a text, including figurative language such as metaphors and similes. **Language 4.a.** Use context (e.g., cause/effect relationships and comparisons in text) as a clue to the meaning of a word or phrase. **Language 5.c.** Use the relationships between particular words (e.g., synonyms, antonyms, homographs) to better understand each of the words.

Next

Name _____

Writing – Constructed Response

Based on the information in the passage from the selection *Island of the Blue Dolphins,* write a paragraph about the narrator's choice of location to build her house. Do you agree with her plan or not? Why?

State your opinion and support it with reasons. Use your own ideas as well as details from the text. Conclude with a sentence that restates your opinion. Remember to check your writing for correct capitalization, punctuation, and spelling.

_____

_____

_____

_____

_____

_____

_____

_____

_____

_____

_____

_____

To the Teacher: Use the Writing Rubric on page T17 to assess students' writing.

COMMON CORE STATE STANDARDS

Literature 1. Quote accurately from a text when explaining what the text says explicitly and when drawing inferences from the text. **Writing 1.** Write opinion pieces on topics or texts, supporting a point of view with reasons and information. **Writing 1.a.** Introduce a topic or text clearly, state an opinion, and create an organizational structure in which ideas are logically grouped to support the writer's purpose. **Writing 1.b.** Provide logically ordered reasons that are supported by facts and details. **Writing 4.** Produce clear and coherent writing in which the development and organization are appropriate to task, purpose, and audience. **Writing 9.** Draw evidence from literary or informational texts to support analysis, reflection, and research. **Language 2.** Demonstrate command of the conventions of standard English capitalization, punctuation, and spelling when writing.

Next

Writing – Extended Response

You have read two texts about courageous, resourceful young women.

- *Island of the Blue Dolphins*
- *Thunder Rose*

Compare and contrast the two main characters in the texts, the narrator in *Island of the Blue Dolphins* and Rose in *Thunder Rose*. Write an essay in which you tell how the characters are alike and how they are different. Introduce the topic and then develop it with facts, details, and examples from the selections. Provide a concluding statement that sums up your main points. When you have finished, read your paragraph carefully and correct any errors in grammar, capitalization, punctuation, and spelling.

To the Teacher: Tell students they may use the space on this page to plan their writing. Then have them write their response on the following pages. Use the Writing Rubric on page T18 to assess students' writing.

COMMON CORE STATE STANDARDS

Literature 3. Compare and contrast two or more characters, settings, or events in a story or drama, drawing on specific details in the text (e.g., how characters interact). **Writing 2.** Write informative/explanatory texts to examine a topic and convey ideas and information clearly. **Writing 2.a.** Introduce a topic clearly, provide a general observation and focus, and group related information logically; include formatting (e.g., headings), illustrations, and multimedia when useful to aiding comprehension. **Writing 2.b.** Develop the topic with facts, definitions, concrete details, quotations, or other information and examples related to the topic. **Writing 4.** Produce clear and coherent writing in which the development and organization are appropriate to task, purpose, and audience. **Writing 9.** Draw evidence from literary or informational texts to support analysis, reflection, and research. **Writing 9.a.** Apply *grade 5 Reading standards* to literature (e.g., "Compare and contrast two or more characters, settings, or events in a story or a drama, drawing on specific details in the text [e.g., how characters interact]"). **Language 1.** Demonstrate command of the conventions of standard English grammar and usage when writing or speaking. **Language 2.** Demonstrate command of the conventions of standard English capitalization, punctuation, and spelling when writing.

Next

Name _____

_____

_____

_____

_____

_____

_____

_____

_____

_____

_____

_____

_____

_____

_____

_____

_____

_____

_____

Next

_____

_____

_____

_____

_____

_____

_____

_____

_____

_____

_____

_____

_____

_____

_____

_____

_____

_____

Directions: Read the following passage. Use information from the passage to answer the questions.

Satchel Paige
by Lesa Cline-Ransome

"Give it to 'em, Satch. Show your stuff," fans and teammates would shout. And he did. Every time. Folks would pack the stands to see how many Satchel could strike out in one game. He made the crowds laugh with his fast talking and slow walking ("A man's got to go slow to go long and far," he'd say), but mostly he made them cheer. (**1**) Never in his nineteen years had he heard a sweeter sound. The more cheers he heard, the more his confidence grew. A kind of confidence that made him call to the outfield with the bases loaded and the last hitter up to bat, "Why don't you all have a seat. Won't be needing you on this one."

Wherever the crowds went, a good paycheck followed, so he made sure to keep them coming. After just one year he was playing in the Negro major leagues for the Chattanooga Black Lookouts, and the folks were still cheering and shouting, "Give it to 'em, Satch. Show your stuff."

There were two major leagues back in 1924, when Satchel was called up. (**2**) Because the white major-league ball clubs wouldn't allow blacks to play in their leagues, blacks had created their own in 1920 and named them the Negro Leagues. The white major-league players enjoyed trains, hotels, hot meals, and short seasons.

Negro League players were often refused meals in restaurants and rooms in hotels. They ate on the road and slept where they could—in train depots or on baseball fields. (**3**) They played two, sometimes three games a day, nearly every day, in a season as long as the weather would hold. And when the season ended in America, Satch went right on playing and traveling in other parts of the world.

Life in the Negro Leagues suited Satchel. He was a traveling man. One city could never hold him for long. He moved from Alabama, where he played with the Birmingham Black Barons, to Tennessee, where he played with the Nashville Elite Giants, and to Pennsylvania, where he played with the Pittsburgh Crawfords.

Next

From the first breath of spring till the cool rush of fall he would ride. Sometimes he joined his teammates on rickety old buses, bumping along on back roads studded with potholes so deep, players would have to hold on to their seats (and stomachs) just to keep from spilling into the aisles. **(4)** But mostly he drove alone, in cars that would take him wherever he wanted to go. The fans would always be waiting in the next town. Their wait could be a long one—he was never much for keeping anyone's time but his own.

Once he reached his mid-thirties, the joys of traveling began to wear thin for Satchel. He found himself longing for a more settled life and the comforts of a home. In 1941 he finally found it in the warm smile and tender heart of Lahoma Brown. Satch rested his travel-weary legs and happily began his second career as husband and father. But even though he had finally found what he thought he'd been searching for, it was only a year before he took to the road again with his first and only true love—baseball. His family would have to wait.

Next

Text-Based Comprehension

Directions: Read the questions below and choose the best answer.

1. **Part A**

Reread the numbered sentences in the passage. Which sentence is an opinion?

○ **A.** sentence 1
○ **B.** sentence 2
○ **C.** sentence 3
○ **D.** sentence 4

Part B

Which words from the sentence helped you identify it as an opinion?

○ **A.** mostly, wherever
○ **B.** because, their own
○ **C.** never, sweeter
○ **D.** sometimes, as long as

COMMON CORE STATE STANDARDS

Informational Text 1. Quote accurately from a text when explaining what the text says explicitly and when drawing inferences from the text. **Informational Text 8.** Explain how an author uses reasons and evidence to support particular points in a text, identifying which reasons and evidence support which point(s).

Next

2. **Part A**

What is the unstated main idea of the last paragraph?

○ **A.** Satchel began to grow tired of traveling so much of the time.

○ **B.** Satchel married Lahoma Brown and started a new career.

○ **C.** A settled life did not suit Satchel as well as he thought it would.

○ **D.** After a year, Satchel went back to traveling and playing baseball.

Part B

Which sentence from the paragraph supports this main idea?

○ **A.** "Once he reached his mid-thirties, the joys of traveling began to wear thin for Satchel."

○ **B.** "In 1941 he finally found it in the warm smile and tender heart of Lahoma Brown."

○ **C.** "Satch rested his travel-weary legs and happily began his second career as husband and father."

○ **D.** "The family would have to wait."

COMMON CORE STATE STANDARDS

Informational Text 1. Quote accurately from a text when explaining what the text says explicitly and when drawing inferences from the text. **Informational Text 2.** Determine two or more main ideas of a text and explain how they are supported by key details; summarize the text.

Next

3. **Part A**

   What caused Satchel to feel more and more confident?

   ○ **A.** his teammates' laughter
   ○ **B.** the shouting fans
   ○ **C.** a good paycheck
   ○ **D.** the way he talked to hitters

   Part B

   Which sentence from the passage supports your answer to Part A?

   ○ **A.** "The more cheers he heard, the more his confidence grew."
   ○ **B.** "There were two major leagues back in 1924, when Satchel was called up."
   ○ **C.** "Life in the Negro Leagues suited Satchel."
   ○ **D.** "From the first breath of spring till the cool rush of fall he would ride."

COMMON CORE STATE STANDARDS

Informational Text 1. Quote accurately from a text when explaining what the text says explicitly and when drawing inferences from the text. **Informational Text 3.** Explain the relationships or interactions between two or more individuals, events, ideas, or concepts in a historical, scientific, or technical text based on specific information in the text.

Vocabulary

Directions: Read the questions below and choose the best answer.

4. **Part A**

Which word is an antonym for the word "rickety" in the following sentence?

"Sometimes he joined his teammates on rickety old buses, bumping along on back roads studded with potholes so deep, players would have to hold on to their seats (and stomachs) just to keep from spilling into the aisles."

- ○ **A.** noisy
- ○ **B.** shaky
- ○ **C.** large
- ○ **D.** sturdy

Part B

Which detail from the passage helped you choose the antonym in Part A?

- ○ **A.** "cool rush"
- ○ **B.** "old buses"
- ○ **C.** "so deep"
- ○ **D.** "back roads"

COMMON CORE STATE STANDARDS

Informational Text 4. Determine the meaning of general academic and domain-specific words and phrases in a text relevant to a *grade 5 topic or subject area.* **Language 4.a.** Use context (e.g., cause/effect relationships and comparisons in text) as a clue to the meaning of a word or phrase. **Language 5.c.** Use the relationships between particular words (e.g., synonyms, antonyms, homographs) to better understand each of the words.

Next

5. **Part A**

What is the meaning of the idiom "to wear thin" in the last paragraph?

- ○ **A.** to become stronger or more intense
- ○ **B.** to put on lightweight clothing
- ○ **C.** to become weak or ready to give way
- ○ **D.** to seem to be skinnier than usual

Part B

Which context clue helped you figure out the meaning of the idiom?

- ○ **A.** "found himself longing for"
- ○ **B.** "a more settled life"
- ○ **C.** "the comforts of a home"
- ○ **D.** "reached his mid-thirties"

COMMON CORE STATE STANDARDS

Informational Text 4. Determine the meaning of general academic and domain-specific words and phrases in a text relevant to a *grade 5 topic or subject area*. **Language 4.a.** Use context (e.g., cause/effect relationships and comparisons in text) as a clue to the meaning of a word or phrase. **Language 5.b.** Recognize and explain the meaning of common idioms, adages, and proverbs.

Next

6. **Part A**

What is the best definition of the word "refused" in the following sentence?

"Negro League players were often refused meals in restaurants and rooms in hotels."

- ○ **A.** not paid back
- ○ **B.** permitted
- ○ **C.** not allowed
- ○ **D.** ordered

Part B

Which context clue from the passage does **not** help you answer Part A?

- ○ **A.** "white major-league players enjoyed"
- ○ **B.** "two, sometimes three games a day"
- ○ **C.** "ate on the road"
- ○ **D.** "slept where they could"

COMMON CORE STATE STANDARDS

Informational Text 4. Determine the meaning of general academic and domain-specific words and phrases in a text relevant to a *grade 5 topic or subject area.* **Language 4.a.** Use context (e.g., cause/effect relationships and comparisons in text) as a clue to the meaning of a word or phrase. **Language 5.c.** Use the relationships between particular words (e.g., synonyms, antonyms, homographs) to better understand each of the words.

Next

Writing – Constructed Response

Based on the information in the passage from the selection *Satchel Paige,* write a short description of a typical day in the life of a Negro League baseball player in the 1920s.

Introduce the topic and then develop it using details from the text. Conclude with a sentence that sums up the description. After writing, review your work and correct any errors in grammar, capitalization, punctuation, and spelling.

_____

_____

_____

_____

_____

_____

_____

_____

_____

_____

_____

To the Teacher: Use the Writing Rubric on page T17 to assess students' writing.

COMMON CORE STATE STANDARDS

Informational Text 1. Quote accurately from a text when explaining what the text says explicitly and when drawing inferences from the text. **Writing 2.** Write informative/explanatory texts to examine a topic and convey ideas and information clearly. **Writing 2.a.** Introduce a topic clearly, provide a general observation and focus, and group related information logically; include formatting (e.g., headings), illustrations, and multimedia when useful to aiding comprehension. **Writing 2.b.** Develop the topic with facts, definitions, concrete details, quotations, or other information and examples related to the topic. **Writing 2.e.** Provide a concluding statement or section related to the information or explanation presented. **Writing 4.** Produce clear and coherent writing in which the development and organization are appropriate to task, purpose, and audience. **Writing 9.** Draw evidence from literary or informational texts to support analysis, reflection, and research. **Language 1.** Demonstrate command of the conventions of standard English grammar and usage when writing or speaking. **Language 2.** Demonstrate command of the conventions of standard English capitalization, punctuation, and spelling when writing.

Next

Writing – Extended Response

You have read two texts about extraordinary baseball players who overcame obstacles to play the sport they loved.

- *Satchel Paige*
- "Roberto Clemente: A Baseball Hero"

Imagine that Satchel Paige and Roberto Clemente have dinner together and talk about their lives and careers. Write their conversation using facts and details from both texts. Establish the situation and introduce the characters. Use dialogue and description to show how the characters respond to experiences and events. Remember to follow the conventions of standard English grammar. Be sure to check your writing for correct capitalization, punctuation, and spelling.

To the Teacher: Tell students they may use the space on this page to plan their writing. Then have them write their response on the following pages. Use the Writing Rubric on page T18 to assess students' writing.

COMMON CORE STATE STANDARDS

Informational Text 1. Quote accurately from a text when explaining what the text says explicitly and when drawing inferences from the text. **Writing 3.** Write narratives to develop real or imagined experiences or events using effective technique, descriptive details, and clear event sequence. **Writing 3.a.** Orient the reader by establishing a situation and introducing a narrator and/or characters; organize an event sequence that unfolds naturally. **Writing 3.b.** Use narrative techniques, such as dialogue, description, and pacing, to develop experiences and events or show the responses of characters to situations. **Writing 4.** Produce clear and coherent writing in which the development and organization are appropriate to task, purpose, and audience. **Writing 9.** Draw evidence from literary or informational texts to support analysis, reflection, and research. **Language 1.** Demonstrate command of the conventions of standard English grammar and usage when writing or speaking. **Language 2.** Demonstrate command of the conventions of standard English capitalization, punctuation, and spelling when writing.

Next

Name _____

_____

_____

_____

_____

_____

_____

_____

_____

_____

_____

_____

_____

_____

_____

_____

_____

_____

_____

Next

_____

_____

_____

_____

_____

_____

_____

_____

_____

_____

_____

_____

_____

_____

_____

_____

_____

_____

Name _____

Directions: Read the following passage. Use information from the passage to answer the questions.

Ten Mile Day and the Building of the Transcontinental Railroad

by Mary Ann Fraser

At 1:30 the whistle sounded, calling a halt for lunch. Whirlwind No. 62, the Pioneer Train locomotive, pushed the kitchen cars up, and the boarding boss served hot boiled beef.

A quick measurement showed that six miles of track had already been laid, spiked, and bolted that morning. Whoops and hollers went up as the news spread among the men. They were now confident they could reach their goal of ten miles in one day, and they named their rest stop Camp Victory.

At 2:30 work began again, but a special crew had to be called in. The tracks were now climbing the west slope of the Promontory Mountains. The climb was steep and full of curves, and the rails had to be bent.

Lacking measuring instruments, this new crew judged the curves by sight. They jammed the rails between blocks and then slowly and carefully hammered them into the right shapes. Every rail now took extra time to mold and fit.

As the afternoon wore on, the foreman continued to ride the line, encouraging the men. Although the horses pulling the iron cars were changed every two hours, they could no longer run up the grade. Now they had to walk slowly up the steep hillside. The rail gang was dripping with sweat, and their muscles must have burned from overuse, but not one man stopped to rest. With each hour another mile of track reached toward Promontory Summit.

By 7 P.M. the sun was dipping behind Monument Point. Strobridge signaled for the final blast from the train whistle. The exhausted men cast down their tools, and the day's work came to an abrupt end.

How much rail had the men of the Central Pacific laid? Two Union Pacific engineers took out their surveying chains and began to measure. Everyone waited for the final count. Then it came. The railhead was ten miles, fifty-six feet farther east than it had been the previous evening.

The crews flung their hats into the air, cheering and shaking hands all around. They had done the impossible again. The Union Pacific's record was destroyed, and Thomas Durant lost the bet. A total of 3,520 rails, twice that number of fishplates, 28,160 spikes, and 14,080 nuts and bolts had been placed to complete the job.

The eight track layers were declared heroes and were featured in later histories. Each had lifted over 125 tons of iron. No single crew has ever beaten their record. The Chinese workers had once again proven themselves to their biased rivals. Each team had something to celebrate.

Next

Text-Based Comprehension

Directions: Read the questions below and choose the best answer.

1. **Part A**

   What caused the workers to whoop and holler at lunchtime?

   ○ **A.** They were grateful it was time to rest and eat.

   ○ **B.** They heard good news.

   ○ **C.** They wanted to continue working.

   ○ **D.** They realized they were behind schedule.

   Part B

   Which sentence from the passage supports your answer to Part A?

   ○ **A.** "At 1:30 the whistle sounded, calling a halt for lunch."

   ○ **B.** "Whirlwind No. 62 . . . pushed the kitchen cars up, and the boarding boss served hot boiled beef."

   ○ **C.** "A quick measurement showed that six miles of track had already been laid, spiked, and bolted that morning."

   ○ **D.** "At 2:30 work began again, but a special crew had to be called in."

COMMON CORE STATE STANDARDS

Informational Text 1. Quote accurately from a text when explaining what the text says explicitly and when drawing inferences from the text. **Informational Text 3.** Explain the relationships or interactions between two or more individuals, events, ideas, or concepts in a historical, scientific, or technical text based on specific information in the text.

Next

2. **Part A**

Which was an effect caused by the Central Pacific workers laying ten miles of track in one day?

- ○ **A.** Union Pacific president Thomas Durant won a lot of money.
- ○ **B.** The Central Pacific workers beat the Union Pacific workers.
- ○ **C.** The transcontinental railroad was completed sooner than expected.
- ○ **D.** There was a shortage of rails, fishplates, spikes, nuts, and bolts.

Part B

Which sentence from the passage supports your answer to Part A?

- ○ **A.** "The Union Pacific's record was destroyed, and Thomas Durant lost the bet."
- ○ **B.** "The exhausted men cast down their tools, and the day's work came to an abrupt end."
- ○ **C.** "Two Union Pacific engineers took out their surveying chains and began to measure."
- ○ **D.** "A total of 3,520 rails, twice that number of fishplates, 28,160 spikes, and 14,080 nuts and bolts had been placed to complete the job."

COMMON CORE STATE STANDARDS

Informational Text 1. Quote accurately from a text when explaining what the text says explicitly and when drawing inferences from the text. **Informational Text 3.** Explain the relationships or interactions between two or more individuals, events, ideas, or concepts in a historical, scientific, or technical text based on specific information in the text.

Next

3. **Part A**

What can you infer about the Central Pacific workers at the end of the ten-mile day?

○ **A.** They were disappointed with the final results.

○ **B.** They vowed to never work for a railroad again.

○ **C.** They disputed the Union Pacific's measurement.

○ **D.** They were proud of what they had accomplished.

Part B

Which sentence from the passage supports this inference?

○ **A.** "As the afternoon wore on, the foreman continued to ride the line, encouraging the men."

○ **B.** "They jammed the rails between blocks and then slowly and carefully hammered them into the right shapes."

○ **C.** "The crews flung their hats into the air, cheering and shaking hands all around."

○ **D.** "The exhausted men cast down their tools, and the day's work came to an abrupt end."

COMMON CORE STATE STANDARDS

Informational Text 1. Quote accurately from a text when explaining what the text says explicitly and when drawing inferences from the text.

Next

Vocabulary

Directions: Read the questions below and choose the best answer.

4. **Part A**

   Which meaning of the word "record" is used in the last paragraph?

   ○ **A.** official written account
   ○ **B.** known facts about a person or a group
   ○ **C.** thin, flat disk played on a phonograph
   ○ **D.** best amount, rate, or speed yet reached

   Part B

   Which word from the paragraph is the best clue to the meaning of "record"?

   ○ **A.** single
   ○ **B.** beaten
   ○ **C.** histories
   ○ **D.** crew

COMMON CORE STATE STANDARDS

Informational Text 4. Determine the meaning of general academic and domain-specific words and phrases in a text relevant to a *grade 5 topic or subject area.* **Language 4.** Determine or clarify the meaning of unknown and multiple-meaning words and phrases based on *grade 5 reading and content,* choosing flexibly from a range of strategies. **Language 4.a.** Use context (e.g., cause/effect relationships and comparisons in text) as a clue to the meaning of a word or phrase.

Next

Name _____

5. **Part A**

Which word is a synonym for the word "cast" in the following sentence?

"The exhausted men cast down their tools, and the day's work came to an abrupt end."

○ **A.** threw

○ **B.** shaped

○ **C.** selected

○ **D.** fell

Part B

Which word from the passage helped you choose the synonym in Part A?

○ **A.** tools

○ **B.** exhausted

○ **C.** down

○ **D.** blast

COMMON CORE STATE STANDARDS

Informational Text 4. Determine the meaning of general academic and domain-specific words and phrases in a text relevant to a *grade 5 topic or subject area.* **Language 4.** Determine or clarify the meaning of unknown and multiple-meaning words and phrases based on *grade 5 reading and content,* choosing flexibly from a range of strategies. **Language 4.a.** Use context (e.g., cause/effect relationships and comparisons in text) as a clue to the meaning of a word or phrase. **Language 5.c.** Use the relationships between particular words (e.g., synonyms, antonyms, homographs) to better understand each of the words.

Next

6. **Part A**

What is the best definition for the word "grade" as it is used in the following sentence?

"Although the horses pulling the iron cars were changed every two hours, they could no longer run up the grade."

- ○ **A.** division of school
- ○ **B.** slope or incline
- ○ **C.** degree of quality
- ○ **D.** mark on test or paper

Part B

Which context clue from the passage helped you answer Part A?

- ○ **A.** "changed every two hours"
- ○ **B.** "no longer"
- ○ **C.** "the steep hillside"
- ○ **D.** "dripping with sweat"

COMMON CORE STATE STANDARDS

Informational Text 4. Determine the meaning of general academic and domain-specific words and phrases in a text relevant to a *grade 5 topic or subject area.* **Language 4.** Determine or clarify the meaning of unknown and multiple-meaning words and phrases based on *grade 5 reading and content,* choosing flexibly from a range of strategies. **Language 4.a.** Use context (e.g., cause/effect relationships and comparisons in text) as a clue to the meaning of a word or phrase. **Language 5.c.** Use the relationships between particular words (e.g., synonyms, antonyms, homographs) to better understand each of the words.

Next

Writing – Constructed Response

Based on the information in the passage from the selection *Ten Mile Day and the Building of the Transcontinental Railroad,* write a journal entry for April 28, 1869. Imagine that you are there at 7 P.M. when the final whistle blows and the Central Pacific crews stop working. Tell what happens next.

Describe the setting and organize the events in a clear sequence. Use sensory details to convey what the experience is like. Check your writing for correct capitalization, punctuation, and spelling.

_____

_____

_____

_____

_____

_____

_____

_____

_____

_____

_____

_____

To the Teacher: Use the Writing Rubric on page T17 to assess students' writing.

COMMON CORE STATE STANDARDS

Informational Text 1. Quote accurately from a text when explaining what the text says explicitly and when drawing inferences from the text. **Writing 3.** Write narratives to develop real or imagined experiences or events using effective technique, descriptive details, and clear event sequence. **Writing 3.a.** Orient the reader by establishing a situation and introducing a narrator and/or characters; organize an event sequence that unfolds naturally. **Writing 3.d.** Use concrete words and phrases and sensory details to convey experiences and events precisely. **Writing 4.** Produce clear and coherent writing in which the development and organization are appropriate to task, purpose, and audience. **Writing 9.** Draw evidence from literary or informational texts to support analysis, reflection, and research. **Language 2.** Demonstrate command of the conventions of standard English capitalization, punctuation, and spelling when writing.

Next

Writing – Extended Response

You have read two texts about important projects and the people who worked hard to complete them.

- *Ten Mile Day and the Building of the Transcontinental Railroad*
- *Island of the Blue Dolphins*

Write an opinion essay in which you defend this idea.

A project will be successful only if it is completed using a carefully planned step-by-step process.

Begin by introducing the topic and stating your opinion. Then offer two or more reasons, each supported by details, facts, and examples from the texts. Provide a concluding sentence that restates your opinion. When you have finished, read your paragraph carefully and correct any errors in grammar, capitalization, punctuation, and spelling.

To the Teacher: Tell students they may use the space on this page to plan their writing. Then have them write their response on the following pages. Use the Writing Rubric on page T18 to assess students' writing.

COMMON CORE STATE STANDARDS

Writing 1. Write opinion pieces on topics or texts, supporting a point of view with reasons and information. **Writing 1.a.** Introduce a topic or text clearly, state an opinion, and create an organizational structure in which ideas are logically grouped to support the writer's purpose. **Writing 1.b.** Provide logically ordered reasons that are supported by facts and details. **Writing 1.d.** Provide a concluding statement or section related to the opinion presented. **Writing 4.** Produce clear and coherent writing in which the development and organization are appropriate to task, purpose, and audience. **Writing 9.** Draw evidence from literary or informational texts to support analysis, reflection, and research. **Language 1.** Demonstrate command of the conventions of standard English grammar and usage when writing or speaking. **Language 2.** Demonstrate command of the conventions of standard English capitalization, punctuation, and spelling when writing.

Name _____

_____

_____

_____

_____

_____

_____

_____

_____

_____

_____

_____

_____

_____

_____

_____

_____

_____

_____

Next

Directions: Read the following passage. Use information from the passage to answer the questions.

At the Beach
by Lulu Delacre

"Watch out for sea urchins!" I warned as I led the group on our climb. The spiny black sea urchins hid inside the crevices and crannies of the rough boulders. It was very painful if you stepped on one. Luisa and Mari followed behind me. They were careful to only step on the rocks I stepped on. Little Javi came last. He stopped constantly to look at the *cobitos,* the tiny hermit crabs that scurried around on the rocks, and at the iridescent tropical fish that were concealed in the deepest tide pools. I had to keep checking behind me to make sure he didn't stray from the path.

Just then, I turned around to watch helplessly as Javi slipped on an algae-covered rock. *"¡Cuidado!"* I warned. But it was too late.

"¡Ay!" he shrieked and then began to cry uncontrollably.

Cautiously, we all hurried back to help Javi. Luisa and Mari crouched down to examine his foot.

"He stepped on a sea urchin!" Mari cried. "Now what are we going to do?"

"We should have never followed you," Luisa lamented. "We'll all be punished."

At that moment I did not want to think of what the punishment would be. What if we couldn't have any of Mami's tortilla? All I knew was that we had to help Javi right away. I looked around and found a piece of driftwood.

"Luisa," I ordered. "Hold his leg still while I remove the urchin from his foot."

Luisa held Javi's leg still as Mari held his hand and tried to comfort him. But Javi's desperate cries were now drowning out the sound of the sea.

I pulled and tugged, but the urchin wouldn't budge. It was stuck to Javi's foot by the tips of its spines. Javi was scared and in pain. And we were too far away from our parents to ask for help. What if we couldn't get Javi back? I struggled relentlessly until I was finally able to remove the spiny creature from his foot.

Gently, Luisa poured some seawater over Javi's foot. That was when she noticed there was still a piece of the sea urchin's spine lodged in it. Javi wasn't going to be able to walk back, and he was much too heavy for us to carry. We had to remove that piece of spine so that he could walk on his own.

Next

The sun burnt our backs as we all took turns trying to dislodge the sea urchin's spine.

"I have an idea," said Luisa suddenly. She removed her hair barrettes and held them like tweezers. Then, with the smallest movement, she pulled the broken spine out. With that solved, we started back.

I helped Javi walk on his sore foot. He wept and limped with every step. Our walk back seemed endless. As we got closer I realized that we would have to explain how it was that we went to the reef in the first place. I would surely end up with no tortilla if we told the truth.

"What will we do now?" Mari asked.

"We'll have to tell our parents what happened," said Luisa matter-of-factly.

"No!" I said emphatically. "We'll be punished for sure."

Next

Text-Based Comprehension

Directions: Read the questions below and choose the best answer.

1. **Part A**

   Which of the following details is revealed by the narrator's thoughts?

   ○ **A.** Sea urchins have large, poisonous teeth.

   ○ **B.** Algae-covered rocks are sharp.

   ○ **C.** The children's parents will be proud.

   ○ **D.** Stepping on a sea urchin is dangerous.

   Part B

   Which sentence from the passage best supports your answer to Part A?

   ○ **A.** "All I knew was that we had to help Javi right away."

   ○ **B.** "Javi slipped on an algae-covered rock."

   ○ **C.** "'We'll all be punished.'"

   ○ **D.** "I led the group on our climb."

COMMON CORE STATE STANDARDS

Literature 1. Quote accurately from a text when explaining what the text says explicitly and when drawing inferences from the text. **Literature 6.** Describe how a narrator's or speaker's point of view influences how events are described.

Next

2. **Part A**

Which statement best compares the narrator and Luisa?

- ○ **A.** Both help Javi.
- ○ **B.** Both want to lie.
- ○ **C.** Both carry Javi.
- ○ **D.** Both step on a sea urchin.

Part B

Which detail from the passage best supports your answer to Part A?

- ○ **A.** "'be punished for sure'"
- ○ **B.** "poured some seawater over Javi's foot"
- ○ **C.** "scared and in pain"
- ○ **D.** "as I led the group on our climb"

COMMON CORE STATE STANDARDS

Literature 1. Quote accurately from a text when explaining what the text says explicitly and when drawing inferences from the text. **Literature 3.** Compare and contrast two or more characters, settings, or events in a story or drama, drawing on specific details in the text (e.g., how characters interact).

Next

Name _____

3. **Part A**

What is a main theme of this passage?

○ **A.** It is better to lead than follow.

○ **B.** Always be prepared.

○ **C.** Actions have consequences.

○ **D.** The future is hard to predict.

Part B

Which sentence from the passage best supports this theme?

○ **A.** "I would surely end up with no tortilla if we told the truth."

○ **B.** "He stopped constantly to look at the *cobitos*. . . ."

○ **C.** "They were careful to only step on the rocks I stepped on."

○ **D.** "She removed her hair barrettes and held them like tweezers."

COMMON CORE STATE STANDARDS

Literature 1. Quote accurately from a text when explaining what the text says explicitly and when drawing inferences from the text. **Literature 2.** Determine a theme of a story, drama, or poem from details in the text, including how characters in a story or drama respond to challenges or how the speaker in a poem reflects upon a topic; summarize the text.

Next

Vocabulary

Directions: Read the questions below and choose the best answer.

4. **Part A**

What are "crevices" and "crannies"?

○ **A.** two kinds of small sea creatures

○ **B.** small, narrow openings or cracks

○ **C.** cousins and grandparents

○ **D.** small ocean waves that fill tide pools

Part B

Which detail from the passage helped you answer Part A?

○ **A.** "hid inside"

○ **B.** "spiny black"

○ **C.** "deepest tide pools"

○ **D.** "on our climb"

COMMON CORE STATE STANDARDS

Literature 4. Determine the meaning of words and phrases as they are used in a text, including figurative language such as metaphors and similes. **Language 4.** Determine or clarify the meaning of unknown and multiple-meaning words and phrases based on *grade 5 reading and content,* choosing flexibly from a range of strategies. **Language 4.a.** Use context (e.g., cause/effect relationships and comparisons in text) as a clue to the meaning of a word or phrase.

Next

5. **Part A**

Which meaning of the word "lodged" is used in the following sentence?

"That was when she noticed there was still a piece of the sea urchin's spine lodged in it."

○ **A.** put before some authority

○ **B.** lived somewhere for a time

○ **C.** got caught somewhere

○ **D.** rented a room in another's house

Part B

Which word from the passage helped you figure out the meaning of "lodged"?

○ **A.** gently

○ **B.** scared

○ **C.** noticed

○ **D.** stuck

COMMON CORE STATE STANDARDS

Literature 4. Determine the meaning of words and phrases as they are used in a text, including figurative language such as metaphors and similes. **Language 4.** Determine or clarify the meaning of unknown and multiple-meaning words and phrases based on *grade 5 reading and content,* choosing flexibly from a range of strategies. **Language 4.a.** Use context (e.g., cause/effect relationships and comparisons in text) as a clue to the meaning of a word or phrase. **Language 5.c.** Use the relationships between particular words (e.g., synonyms, antonyms, homographs) to better understand each of the words.

Next

6. **Part A**

What is the meaning of "budge" as it is used in the following sentence?

"I pulled and tugged, but the urchin wouldn't budge."

- ○ **A.** fight back
- ○ **B.** move
- ○ **C.** save up
- ○ **D.** eat

Part B

Which phrase from the passage helped you answer Part A?

- ○ **A.** "sound of the sea"
- ○ **B.** "pulled and tugged"
- ○ **C.** "too heavy"
- ○ **D.** "no tortilla"

COMMON CORE STATE STANDARDS

Literature 4. Determine the meaning of words and phrases as they are used in a text, including figurative language such as metaphors and similes. **Language 4.** Determine or clarify the meaning of unknown and multiple-meaning words and phrases based on *grade 5 reading and content,* choosing flexibly from a range of strategies. **Language 4.a.** Use context (e.g., cause/effect relationships and comparisons in text) as a clue to the meaning of a word or phrase. **Language 5.c.** Use the relationships between particular words (e.g., synonyms, antonyms, homographs) to better understand each of the words.

Next

Writing – Constructed Response

Based on the information in the passage from the selection *At the Beach,* write a paragraph about the narrator's intentions. Apparently he does not plan to tell the adults the truth about what happened. Do you think this is a good idea or a bad idea? Why?

Begin by introducing your topic. State your opinion and support it with reasons. Use your own ideas as well as details from the text. Connect your opinion with reasons using words such as *consequently, for this reason,* or *therefore.* Conclude with a sentence that restates your opinion. After you finish writing, read your paragraph and correct mistakes in grammar, capitalization, punctuation, and spelling.

_____

_____

_____

_____

_____

_____

_____

_____

_____

_____

To the Teacher: Use the Writing Rubric on page T17 to assess students' writing.

COMMON CORE STATE STANDARDS

Literature 1. Quote accurately from a text when explaining what the text says explicitly and when drawing inferences from the text. **Writing 1.** Write opinion pieces on topics or texts, supporting a point of view with reasons and information. **Writing 1.a.** Introduce a topic or text clearly, state an opinion, and create an organizational structure in which ideas are logically grouped to support the writer's purpose. **Writing 1.c.** Link opinion and reasons using words, phrases, and clauses (e.g., *consequently, specifically*). **Writing 1.d.** Provide a concluding statement or section related to the opinion presented. **Writing 4.** Produce clear and coherent writing in which the development and organization are appropriate to task, purpose, and audience. **Language 1.** Demonstrate command of the conventions of standard English grammar and usage when writing or speaking. **Language 2.** Demonstrate command of the conventions of standard English capitalization, punctuation, and spelling when writing.

Next

Writing – Extended Response

You have read two texts about characters that learn lessons about honesty.

- *At the Beach*
- "The Eagle and the Bat"

Compare and contrast the narrator in *At the Beach* and the bat in "The Eagle and the Bat." Write an essay in which you tell how these characters, their actions, and the lessons they learn are alike and different. Introduce the topic and then develop it with facts, details, and examples from the selections. Link your ideas with words such as *in contrast* and *similarly.* Provide a concluding statement that sums up your main points. Remember to follow the conventions of standard English grammar and use correct punctuation, capitalization, and spelling.

To the Teacher: Tell students they may use the space on this page to plan their writing. Then have them write their response on the following pages. Use the Writing Rubric on page T18 to assess students' writing.

COMMON CORE STATE STANDARDS

Literature 3. Compare and contrast two or more characters, settings, or events in a story or drama, drawing on specific details in the text (e.g., how characters interact). **Writing 2.** Write informative/explanatory texts to examine a topic and convey ideas and information clearly. **Writing 2.a.** Introduce a topic clearly, provide a general observation and focus, and group related information logically; include formatting (e.g., headings), illustrations, and multimedia when useful to aiding comprehension. **Writing 2.b.** Develop the topic with facts, definitions, concrete details, quotations, or other information and examples related to the topic. **Writing 2.c.** Link ideas within and across categories of information using words, phrases, and clauses (e.g., *in contrast, especially*). **Writing 4.** Produce clear and coherent writing in which the development and organization are appropriate to task, purpose, and audience. **Writing 9.** Draw evidence from literary or informational texts to support analysis, reflection, and research. **Language 1.** Demonstrate command of the conventions of standard English grammar and usage when writing or speaking. **Language 2.** Demonstrate command of the conventions of standard English capitalization, punctuation, and spelling when writing.

Name _____

_____

_____

_____

_____

_____

_____

_____

_____

_____

_____

_____

_____

_____

_____

_____

_____

_____

_____

_____

_____

Next

_____

_____

_____

_____

_____

_____

_____

_____

_____

_____

_____

_____

_____

_____

_____

_____

_____

_____

Directions: Read the following passage. Use information from the passage to answer the questions.

Hold the Flag High
by Catherine Clinton

The only thing scarier than a battle is the night before a battle. While soldiers swapped stories and took out pictures of their sweethearts and children, Sergeant William H. Carney strolled among the campfires.

A homesick private played his harmonica sweet and low. Carney draped a blanket around the shoulders of Company C's drummer boy, a young slave who had run off from his master to join the fight. Carney assured him, "Tomorrow's gonna be a big day for us, Ned. You'll be drumming us to glory."

Carney was one of the few black officers in the Massachusetts Fifty-fourth, a new African American regiment formed in the spring of 1863.

Carney's men took pride in the shiny brass buttons on their uniforms and new rifles on their shoulders. Just a few weeks before, they had paraded through the streets of Boston. Ladies had waved handkerchiefs, and all had shouted hurrahs and farewells. Then the Fifty-fourth Regiment had set sail to fight in far-off South Carolina.

Once they arrived, the soldiers set up camp south of Charleston Bay. Their first battle would come tomorrow.

This was the day they had all been waiting for, the soldiers told themselves as they headed off to bed.

Carney kicked out the fire. An owl hooted in the distance. Ned, the drummer boy, wondered if it was really an owl. Maybe it was the signal of a Confederate spy.

"Sarge, I don't know what it'll be like when the Rebs start shootin'. I'm feeling scared—and—and—" he stuttered, "and what if I get lost?"

"Son, you just play that drum, and remember what we're fighting for: Old Glory will lead the way."

"Old Glory?" Ned asked.

"Sure, son, keep your eyes on the flag," said Carney. "Like hundreds before us and thousands after, just follow those Stars and Stripes, and you can't go wrong."

Next

"I can't go wrong," Ned murmured as Carney tucked him into his bedroll.

Then the sergeant said a little prayer, hoping it would be true.

Long before the sun rose, the men of the Fifty-fourth awoke to prepare for the battle. They checked and rechecked their rifles, making sure the flints were dry and the bayonets sharp and shined. Ned worked hard, filling canteens with water.

After a breakfast of hardtack and coffee, each soldier had his name pinned onto the back of his uniform. This way soldiers who did not survive the battle could be identified. Soldiers who could write helped those who couldn't.

Carney tipped his hat at the color-bearer. He was the soldier who carried the regiment's flag into battle on a short flagpole, called a staff. "We're all counting on you, brother."

The wind whipped the banner, held aloft on its staff: back and forth; then again, back and forth.

Soldiers bristled with anticipation.

Ned could see their commanding officer, Robert Gould Shaw, approaching on horseback. As he galloped up, spurs gleaming on his heels and a fringed silk sash across his chest, the colonel seemed to own the day.

But when Shaw dismounted, Ned noticed that his pale face was nearly as white as his stallion. Ned wondered, *Could he be scared, too?*

Maybe Shaw *was* a bit afraid; he had already been wounded in battle once. But his speech to his troops betrayed no fears. Shaw fired up his men for battle. The Fifty-fourth had been picked to lead the charge against Fort Wagner—the Confederate outpost guarding Charleston. Chests swollen with pride, these soldiers could hardly wait. They would gladly follow Shaw to the ends of the Earth, eager to prove their courage under fire.

Text-Based Comprehension

Directions: Read the questions below and choose the best answer.

1. **Part A**

    Which of these events happens early in the morning?

    ○ **A.** Ned asks Carney a question.
    ○ **B.** Carney kicks out the fire.
    ○ **C.** Ned fills canteens with water.
    ○ **D.** A private plays his harmonica.

    Part B

    Which phrase from the passage supports your answer to Part A?

    ○ **A.** "Just a few weeks before"
    ○ **B.** "in the spring of 1863"
    ○ **C.** "Once they arrived"
    ○ **D.** "Long before the sun rose"

COMMON CORE STATE STANDARDS

Informational Text 1. Quote accurately from a text when explaining what the text says explicitly and when drawing inferences from the text. **Informational Text 3.** Explain the relationships or interactions between two or more individuals, events, ideas, or concepts in a historical, scientific, or technical text based on specific information in the text.

Next

2. **Part A**

What effect does Colonel Shaw's speech have on his men?

○ **A.** They are eager to stay in camp.

○ **B.** They are reluctant to follow him.

○ **C.** They are afraid because he is afraid.

○ **D.** They are ready to go into battle.

Part B

Which detail from the passage supports your answer to Part A?

○ **A.** "Chests swollen with pride, these soldiers could hardly wait."

○ **B.** "As he galloped up . . . the colonel seemed to own the day."

○ **C.** "The wind whipped the banner, held aloft on its staff"

○ **D.** "Soldiers who could write helped those who couldn't."

COMMON CORE STATE STANDARDS

Informational Text 1. Quote accurately from a text when explaining what the text says explicitly and when drawing inferences from the text. **Informational Text 3.** Explain the relationships or interactions between two or more individuals, events, ideas, or concepts in a historical, scientific, or technical text based on specific information in the text.

Next

3. **Part A**

What is the main idea of the passage?

○ **A.** The colonel gives a speech that fires up his men for the battle.

○ **B.** The soldiers are both nervous and eager in the hours before the battle.

○ **C.** Sergeant Carney offers advice to the new soldiers before their first battle.

○ **D.** The soldiers prepare their rifles carefully before going into battle.

Part B

Which detail from the passage supports that main idea?

○ **A.** "But his speech to his troops betrayed no fears."

○ **B.** "Then the sergeant said a little prayer, hoping it would be true."

○ **C.** "This was the day they had all been waiting for"

○ **D.** "This way soldiers who did not survive the battle could be identified."

COMMON CORE STATE STANDARDS

Informational Text 1. Quote accurately from a text when explaining what the text says explicitly and when drawing inferences from the text. **Informational Text 2.** Determine two or more main ideas of a text and explain how they are supported by key details; summarize the text.

Next

Vocabulary

Directions: Read the questions below and choose the best answer.

4. **Part A**

Which meaning of the word "private" is used in the following sentence?

"A homesick private played his harmonica sweet and low."

- ○ **A.** intended for a particular person or group
- ○ **B.** not intended to be known publicly
- ○ **C.** low-ranking person in the army
- ○ **D.** shut off from others; secluded

Part B

Which words from the passage are the best clues to the meaning of the word?

- ○ **A.** stories, campfires
- ○ **B.** soldiers, Sergeant
- ○ **C.** sweethearts, homesick
- ○ **D.** blanket, drummer boy

COMMON CORE STATE STANDARDS

Informational Text 4. Determine the meaning of general academic and domain-specific words and phrases in a text relevant to a *grade 5 topic or subject area.* **Language 4.** Determine or clarify the meaning of unknown and multiple-meaning words and phrases based on *grade 5 reading and content,* choosing flexibly from a range of strategies. **Language 4.a.** Use context (e.g., cause/effect relationships and comparisons in text) as a clue to the meaning of a word or phrase. **Language 5.c.** Use the relationship between particular words (e.g., synonyms, antonyms, homographs) to better understand each of the words.

Next

5. **Part A**

What is the best definition of the word "stuttered" in the following dialogue from the passage?

"'Sarge, I don't know what it'll be like when the Rebs start shootin'. I'm feeling scared—and—and—' he stuttered, 'and what if I get lost?'"

○ **A.** repeated in an effort to speak

○ **B.** trembled or quivered with fear

○ **C.** complained or grumbled

○ **D.** shouted in an angry, bitter tone

Part B

Which context clue was most helpful in answering Part A?

○ **A.** "'. . . what if I get lost?'"

○ **B.** "'. . . the Rebs start shootin'.'"

○ **C.** "'. . .—and—and—'"

○ **D.** "'I can't go wrong'"

COMMON CORE STATE STANDARDS

Informational Text 4. Determine the meaning of general academic and domain-specific words and phrases in a text relevant to a *grade 5 topic or subject area.* **Language 4.** Determine or clarify the meaning of unknown and multiple-meaning words and phrases based on *grade 5 reading and content,* choosing flexibly from a range of strategies. **Language 4.a.** Use context (e.g., cause/effect relationships and comparisons in text) as a clue to the meaning of a word or phrase.

Next

6. **Part A**

What is the meaning of the word "dismounted" in the following sentence?

"But when Shaw dismounted, Ned noticed that his pale face was nearly as white as his stallion."

○ **A.** took something away

○ **B.** left something behind

○ **C.** went up something

○ **D.** got off something

Part B

Which context clue helped you figure out the meaning?

○ **A.** "own the day"

○ **B.** "pale face"

○ **C.** "a bit afraid"

○ **D.** "on horseback"

COMMON CORE STATE STANDARDS

Informational Text 4. Determine the meaning of general academic and domain-specific words and phrases in a text relevant to a *grade 5 topic or subject area.* **Language 4.** Determine or clarify the meaning of unknown and multiple-meaning words and phrases based on *grade 5 reading and content,* choosing flexibly from a range of strategies. **Language 4.a.** Use context (e.g., cause/effect relationships and comparisons in text) as a clue to the meaning of a word or phrase.

Next

Name _____

Writing – Constructed Response

Based on the information in the passage from the selection *Hold the Flag High,* write a short description of a day in the life of a Union soldier during the Civil War in the 1860s.

Introduce the topic and then develop it using details from the text. Conclude with a sentence that sums up the description. After you finish writing, reread your description and correct any errors in grammar, capitalization, punctuation, and spelling.

_____

_____

_____

_____

_____

_____

_____

_____

_____

_____

_____

To the Teacher: Use the Writing Rubric on page T17 to assess students' writing.

COMMON CORE STATE STANDARDS

Writing 2. Write informative/explanatory texts to examine a topic and convey ideas and information clearly. **Writing 2.a.** Introduce a topic clearly, provide a general observation and focus, and group related information logically; include formatting (e.g., headings), illustrations, and multimedia when useful to aiding comprehension. **Writing 2.b.** Develop the topic with facts, definitions, concrete details, quotations, or other information and examples related to the topic. **Writing 2.e.** Provide a concluding statement or section related to the information or explanation presented. **Writing 4.** Produce clear and coherent writing in which the development and organization are appropriate to task, purpose, and audience. **Writing 9.** Draw evidence from literary or informational texts to support analysis, reflection, and research. **Language 1.** Demonstrate command of the conventions of standard English grammar and usage when writing or speaking. **Language 2.** Demonstrate command of the conventions of standard English capitalization, punctuation, and spelling when writing.

Next

Writing – Extended Response

You have read two texts in which people must show determination and courage in life-threatening situations.

- *Hold the Flag High*
- *Red Kayak*

Imagine that Ned, the drummer boy in *Hold the Flag High,* meets Brady, the rescuer in *Red Kayak.* They talk about how they faced fear and found courage. Write the dialogue between Ned and Brady using facts and details from both texts. Establish the situation and introduce the characters. Use dialogue and description to show how they responded to their experiences. Remember to follow the conventions of standard English grammar and use correct capitalization, punctuation, and spelling.

To the Teacher: Tell students they may use the space on this page to plan their writing. Then have them write their response on the following pages. Use the Writing Rubric on page T18 to assess students' writing.

COMMON CORE STATE STANDARDS

Writing 3. Write narratives to develop real or imagined experiences or events using effective technique, descriptive details, and clear event sequence. **Writing 3.a.** Orient the reader by establishing a situation and introducing a narrator and/or characters; organize an event sequence that unfolds naturally. **Writing 3.b.** Use narrative techniques, such as dialogue, description, and pacing, to develop experiences and events or show the responses of characters to situations. **Writing 3.d.** Use concrete words and phrases and sensory details to convey experiences and events precisely. **Writing 4.** Produce clear and coherent writing in which the development and organization are appropriate to task, purpose, and audience. **Writing 9.** Draw evidence from literary or informational texts to support analysis, reflection, and research. **Language 1.** Demonstrate command of the conventions of standard English grammar and usage when writing or speaking. **Language 2.** Demonstrate command of the conventions of standard English capitalization, punctuation, and spelling when writing.

Next

Name _____

_____

_____

_____

_____

_____

_____

_____

_____

_____

_____

_____

_____

_____

_____

_____

_____

_____

Next

Name _____

Directions: Read the following passage. Use information from the passage to answer the questions.

The Ch'i-lin Purse

retold by Linda Fang

Mrs. Hsüeh wanted to prepare a dowry for Hsiang-ling that no girl in town could match. But Hsiang-ling was hard to please. Almost everything her mother bought for her was returned or exchanged at least two or three times.

When the dowry was finally complete, Mrs. Hsüeh decided to add one more item to it. It was a Ch'i-lin Purse, a red satin bag embroidered on both sides with a *ch'i-lin,* a legendary animal from ancient times. The *ch'i-lin* had scales all over its body and a single horn on its head. In the old Chinese tradition, the *ch'i-lin* is the symbol of a promising male offspring. Mrs. Hsüeh wanted to give Hsiang-ling the purse because she hoped that her daughter would give birth to a talented son.

When the purse Mrs. Hsüeh had ordered was ready, a family servant brought it home. But Hsiang-ling was not satisfied at all. "I don't like the pattern, take it back!" she said.

The servant returned to the store and ordered another. But when it was brought home, Hsiang-ling merely glanced at it and said, "The colors of the *ch'i-lin* are too dark, take it back!"

The servant went to place another order, but the new purse still did not please her. This time the servant broke down in tears. . . .

Although Hsiang-ling was spoiled, she was not a mean-spirited person. She somehow began to feel sorry for the old man, who had been with her family for more than forty years. So she looked at the purse and said, "All right, I will have this one. You may go and pay for it." The servant went back to the store, paid for the purse, and gave it to Mrs. Hsüeh.

Hsiang-ling's wedding fell on the eighteenth day of the sixth month according to the lunar calendar. It was the day Hsiang-ling had longed for since her engagement. She was very excited and yet a bit sad, because she knew she was leaving her mother and the home she had lived in for sixteen years.

Hsiang-ling wore a red silk dress and a red silk veil over her head. As she sat in her *hua-chiao,* a sedan chair draped with red satin, and waited to be carried to her new home, her mother came to present her with the Ch'i-lin Purse. . . .

Next

She took the purse and laid it on her lap. A few minutes later, four footmen came. Picking up the *hua-chiao,* they placed it on their shoulders, and the wedding procession began.

As the procession reached the road, it started to rain. Soon it was pouring so heavily that the footmen could not see well enough to continue. The wedding procession came to a halt, and the *hua-chiao* was carried into a pavilion that stood alongside the road.

There was another *hua-chiao* in the pavilion. It was shabby, with holes in the drapes. Hsiang-ling could hear a girl sobbing inside. This annoyed her, because she believed that a person crying on her wedding day could bring bad luck. So she told her maid to go and find out what was wrong.

"The bride is very sad," the maid said when she returned. "She is poor and has nothing to take to her new home."

Hsiang-ling couldn't help feeling sorry for the girl. Then her eyes fell on the Ch'i-lin Purse in her lap. She realized that she was lucky to have so many things, while this girl had nothing. Since she wasn't carrying any money with her, she handed the Ch'i-lin Purse to her maid. "Give this to the girl, but don't mention my name."

So the maid went over and gave the purse to the other bride. The girl stopped crying at once. Hsiang-ling had given away her mother's wedding gift without ever finding out what was inside.

Next

Text-Based Comprehension

Directions: Read the questions below and choose the best answer.

1. **Part A**

   Which statement best compares and contrasts the two girls waiting in the pavilion?

   ○ **A.** Both are rich; one has a beautiful *hua-chiao* while the other does not.

   ○ **B.** Both are poor; one is on her way to her new home while the other is not.

   ○ **C.** Both are on their way to their new homes; one is rich while the other is not.

   ○ **D.** Both are on their way to see their mothers; one is traveling in a *hua-chiao* while the other is walking.

   Part B

   Which detail from the passage does **not** support this statement?

   ○ **A.** "It was shabby, with holes in the drapes."

   ○ **B.** "leaving . . . the home she had lived in"

   ○ **C.** "that she was lucky to have so many things"

   ○ **D.** "The wedding procession came to a halt."

COMMON CORE STATE STANDARDS

Literature 1. Quote accurately from a text when explaining what the text says explicitly and when drawing inferences from the text. **Literature 3.** Compare and contrast two or more characters, settings, or events in a story or drama, drawing on specific details in the text (e.g., how characters interact).

Next

2. **Part A**

In the passage, Hsiang-ling is spoiled and hard to please. What keeps her from being a character that readers dislike?

○ **A.** She is annoyed by the crying girl.

○ **B.** She is eager to leave home.

○ **C.** She mistreats the servants.

○ **D.** She is generous to a stranger.

Part B

Which detail from the passage supports your answer to Part A?

○ **A.** "'The colors of the *ch'i-lin* are too dark, take it back!'"

○ **B.** "'Give this to the girl, but don't mention my name.'"

○ **C.** "It was the day Hsiang-ling had longed for."

○ **D.** "A person crying on her wedding day could bring bad luck."

Copyright © Pearson Education, Inc., or its affiliates. All Rights Reserved.

COMMON CORE STATE STANDARDS

Literature 1. Quote accurately from a text when explaining what the text says explicitly and when drawing inferences from the text. **Literature 3.** Compare and contrast two or more characters, settings, or events in a story or drama, drawing on specific details in the text (e.g., how characters interact).

Next

Name _____

3. **Part A**

What inference can you draw about the color red and Chinese culture?

○ **A.** It is worn only by wealthy people.

○ **B.** It is believed to bring good luck.

○ **C.** It is used for all *Ch'i-lin* Purses.

○ **D.** It is used to cover all sedan chairs.

Part B

Which detail from the passage supports this inference?

○ **A.** "the symbol of a promising male offspring"

○ **B.** "the colors of the *ch'i-lin* are too dark"

○ **C.** "wore a red silk dress and a red silk veil"

○ **D.** "crying on her wedding day could bring bad luck"

COMMON CORE STATE STANDARDS

Literature 1. Quote accurately from a text when explaining what the text says explicitly and when drawing inferences from the text.

Next

Vocabulary

Directions: Read the questions below and choose the best answer.

4. **Part A**

The Latin prefix "pro-" means "forward." The Latin word "cedere" means "to go." Use these meanings to figure out the meaning of the word "procession" in the following paragraph.

"She took the purse and laid it on her lap. A few minutes later, four footmen came. Picking up the *hua-chiao,* they placed it on their shoulders, and the wedding procession began."

○ **A.** people sitting at the front

○ **B.** people playing on a team

○ **C.** people marching or riding

○ **D.** people in a particular job

Part B

Which words from the passage also helped you figure out the meaning of the word?

○ **A.** picking and placed

○ **B.** took and laid

○ **C.** returned and ordered

○ **D.** began and halt

COMMON CORE STATE STANDARDS

Literature 4. Determine the meaning of words and phrases as they are used in a text, including figurative language such as metaphors and similes. **Language 4.b.** Use common, grade-appropriate Greek and Latin affixes and roots as clues to the meaning of a word (e.g., *photograph, photosynthesis*).

Next

5. **Part A**

Which meaning of the homograph "scales" is used in the following sentence?

"The *ch'i-lin* had scales all over its body and a single horn on its head."

○ **A.** series of tones that go up or down in pitch

○ **B.** thin plates that form an outer covering on some animals

○ **C.** tools with marks at regular distances, used for measuring

○ **D.** balance with two pans or dishes, used for weighing

Part B

Which words from the passage are the best clue to the meaning of the homograph?

○ **A.** old Chinese tradition

○ **B.** from ancient times

○ **C.** all over its body

○ **D.** on its head

COMMON CORE STATE STANDARDS

Literature 4. Determine the meaning of words and phrases as they are used in a text, including figurative language such as metaphors and similes. **Language 5.c.** Use the relationships between particular words (e.g., synonyms, antonyms, homographs) to better understand each of the words.

Next

6. **Part A**

What is the meaning of the idiom "broke down" in the following sentence?

"This time the servant broke down in tears. . . ."

- ○ **A.** began to cry
- ○ **B.** stopped working
- ○ **C.** failed
- ○ **D.** divided into parts

Part B

Which context clue helped you figure out the meaning of the idiom?

- ○ **A.** servant
- ○ **B.** take back
- ○ **C.** another
- ○ **D.** in tears

COMMON CORE STATE STANDARDS

Literature 4. Determine the meaning of words and phrases as they are used in a text, including figurative language such as metaphors and similes. **Language 5.b.** Recognize and explain the meaning of common idioms, adages, and proverbs.

Next

Name _____

Writing – Constructed Response

Based on the information in the passage from the selection *The Ch'i-lin Purse,* write a new scene for the story. In this scene Hsiang-ling and the other bride talk to each other as they wait in the pavilion.

Use details from the text to establish the situation and present the characters. Use dialogue to show the responses of the characters to each other and to the situation. After you finish writing, read your work carefully and correct any errors in grammar, capitalization, punctuation, and spelling.

_____

_____

_____

_____

_____

_____

_____

_____

_____

_____

To the Teacher: Use the Writing Rubric on page T17 to assess students' writing.

COMMON CORE STATE STANDARDS

Literature 1. Quote accurately from a text when explaining what the text says explicitly and when drawing inferences from the text. **Writing 3.** Write narratives to develop real or imagined experiences or events using effective technique, descriptive details, and clear event sequence. **Writing 3.a.** Orient the reader by establishing a situation and introducing a narrator and/or characters; organize an event sequence that unfolds naturally. **Writing 3.b.** Use narrative techniques, such as dialogue, description, and pacing, to develop experiences and events or show the responses of characters to situations. **Writing 4.** Produce clear and coherent writing in which the development and organization are appropriate to task, purpose, and audience. **Writing 9.** Draw evidence from literary or informational texts to support analysis, reflection, and research. **Language 1.** Demonstrate command of the conventions of standard English grammar and usage when writing or speaking. **Language 2.** Demonstrate command of the conventions of standard English capitalization, punctuation, and spelling when writing.

Next

Writing – Extended Response

You have read two texts about young people who learn important life lessons.

- *The Ch'i-lin Purse*
- *At the Beach*

Think about Hsiang-ling in *The Ch'i-lin Purse* and Fernando, the narrator in *At the Beach,* and about the lesson each character learns. Which lesson do you think is more important, a lesson that all people should learn? Why? Write an opinion piece in which you answer these questions. State your opinion and offer reasons supported by details from the selections and your own ideas. Provide a concluding sentence that restates your opinion. Remember to follow the conventions of standard English grammar and use correct capitalization, punctuation, and spelling.

To the Teacher: Tell students they may use the space on this page to plan their writing. Then have them write their response on the following pages. Use the Writing Rubric on page T18 to assess students' writing.

COMMON CORE STATE STANDARDS

Literature 1. Quote accurately from a text when explaining what the text says explicitly and when drawing inferences from the text. **Writing 1.** Write opinion pieces on topics or texts, supporting a point of view with reasons and information. **Writing 1.a.** Introduce a topic or text clearly, state an opinion, and create an organizational structure in which ideas are logically grouped to support the writer's purpose. **Writing 1.b.** Provide logically ordered reasons that are supported by facts and details. **Writing 1.d.** Provide a concluding statement or section related to the opinion presented. **Writing 4.** Produce clear and coherent writing in which the development and organization are appropriate to task, purpose, and audience. **Writing 9.** Draw evidence from literary or informational texts to support analysis, reflection, and research. **Language 1.** Demonstrate command of the conventions of standard English grammar and usage when writing or speaking. **Language 2.** Demonstrate command of the conventions of standard English capitalization, punctuation, and spelling when writing.

Next

Name _____

_____

_____

_____

_____

_____

_____

_____

_____

_____

_____

_____

_____

_____

_____

_____

_____

_____

_____

_____

_____

_____

_____

_____

_____

_____

_____

_____

_____

_____

_____

_____

_____

_____

_____

_____

_____

_____

Directions: Read the following passage. Use information from the passage to answer the questions.

A Summer's Trade

by Deborah W. Trotter

A dusty pickup bounced along the rutted, dirt road on the Navajo Indian Reservation outside of Gallup, New Mexico. The early morning sun brought out deep red hues in nearby rocks, and yellows and purples on distant mesas. In the passenger seat, Tony barely noticed how the ride jostled him. He had made this long trip to Gallup with his mother many times.

This morning, Tony daydreamed about spending some of his summer days at home on the reservation instead of going into Gallup. He would ride with his father, helping to tend the family's roaming flocks of sheep and goats. But Tony needed a saddle before he could sit for hours on the back of a pony.

In the Trading Post next door to the restaurant where his mother was a waitress, Tony had discovered a beautiful, used saddle for sale. Its dark leather was worn smooth, and there were small nuggets of turquoise laced into the rawhide braid wrapped around the horn. Mr. Hilson, the owner of the Trading Post, invited Tony to help out around the store. In payment, Mr. Hilson put twenty dollars a week into an account for him. As soon as he earned enough money, Tony wanted to buy that saddle. He hoped no one else bought it first.

"Here we are," said his mother, as she parked in front of the Trading Post. Tony got out and slammed the truck door. The high desert wind fluttered the bandana covering his straight, black hair. "Come see me at lunchtime," his mother said. Tony waved as she walked toward the restaurant.

The bell on the door jingled as Tony walked into the Trading Post. "Good morning, Tony," said Mr. Hilson. "Today, I need you to unpack some canned goods and stack them carefully on the store shelves. Then you can sweep out the storage area. It's really dusty back there."

"Okay, Mr. Hilson."

The Trading Post did a lot of business. Tourists came to buy Indian-made goods, such as baskets, pottery, turquoise jewelry, and colorful, woven rugs. Regular customers could buy or trade for just about anything they needed.

Next

Navajos could trade or "pawn" their jewelry in exchange for cash. Some did it because they needed money. Many did it because they wanted their turquoise jewelry to be safe in the Trading Post vault until they needed it for ceremonial wear.

Tony worked hard. There was almost always sweeping to do. Unpacking boxes and stacking things on shelves was a regular job too. If Mr. Hilson was busy, Tony could help customers. He knew where to find everything that was stocked in the Trading Post.

Text-Based Comprehension

Directions: Read the questions below and choose the best answer.

1. **Part A**

   What is one of the author's purposes for writing the first three paragraphs?

   ○ **A.** to give facts about New Mexico's history

   ○ **B.** to present her opinion on an issue

   ○ **C.** to describe the setting of the story

   ○ **D.** to explain the lesson the character learns

   Part B

   Which detail from the text does **not** support your answer to Part A?

   ○ **A.** "in the Trading Post next door to the restaurant"

   ○ **B.** "on the Navajo Indian Reservation outside of Gallup, New Mexico"

   ○ **C.** "The early morning sun brought out deep red hues in nearby rocks."

   ○ **D.** "Mr. Hilson . . . invited Tony to help out around the store."

COMMON CORE STATE STANDARDS

Literature 1. Quote accurately from a text when explaining what the text says explicitly and when drawing inferences from the text.

Next

2. **Part A**

What is the main character's problem in this passage?

○ **A.** He daydreams too much.

○ **B.** He hates going to Gallup.

○ **C.** He doesn't have a saddle.

○ **D.** He has to work in a store.

Part B

Which detail from the passage helped you identify this problem?

○ **A.** "Tony daydreamed about spending some of his summer days at home on the reservation."

○ **B.** "But Tony needed a saddle before he could sit for hours on the back of a pony."

○ **C.** "Tony got out and slammed the truck door."

○ **D.** "In the passenger seat, Tony barely noticed how the ride jostled him."

COMMON CORE STATE STANDARDS

Literature 1. Quote accurately from a text when explaining what the text says explicitly and when drawing inferences from the text.

Next

Name _____

3. **Part A**

Which word best describes Tony as a worker?

○ **A.** capable

○ **B.** lazy

○ **C.** careless

○ **D.** slow

Part B

Which sentence from the passage does **not** support this word choice?

○ **A.** "If Mr. Hilson was busy, Tony could help customers."

○ **B.** "Unpacking boxes and stacking things on shelves was a regular job too."

○ **C.** "There was almost always sweeping to do."

○ **D.** "Navajos could trade or 'pawn' their jewelry in exchange for cash."

COMMON CORE STATE STANDARDS

Literature 1. Quote accurately from a text when explaining what the text says explicitly and when drawing inferences from the text.

Next

Vocabulary

Directions: Read the questions below and choose the best answer.

4. **Part A**

Based on context clues, what does the word "hues" mean in the first paragraph?

○ **A.** lights
○ **B.** rocks
○ **C.** colors
○ **D.** mountains

Part B

Which detail from the paragraph helped you answer Part A?

○ **A.** "dusty . . . rutted, dirt road"
○ **B.** "nearby rocks, and . . . distant mesas"
○ **C.** "early morning sun"
○ **D.** "deep red . . . yellows and purples"

COMMON CORE STATE STANDARDS

Literature 4. Determine the meaning of words and phrases as they are used in a text, including figurative language such as metaphors and similes. **Language 4.** Determine or clarify the meaning of unknown and multiple-meaning words and phrases based on *grade 5 reading and content,* choosing flexibly from a range of strategies. **Language 4.a.** Use context (e.g., cause/effect relationships and comparisons in text) as a clue to the meaning of a word or phrase.

Next

5. **Part A**

Which of the following is a synonym for the word "tend" in the following sentence?

"He would ride with his father, helping to tend the family's roaming flocks of sheep and goats."

○ **A.** begin

○ **B.** care for

○ **C.** pay for

○ **D.** offer

Part B

Which phrase from the passage helped you choose the synonym in Part A?

○ **A.** "flocks of sheep and goats"

○ **B.** "at home on the reservation"

○ **C.** "ride with his father"

○ **D.** "on the back of a pony"

COMMON CORE STATE STANDARDS

Literature 4. Determine the meaning of words and phrases as they are used in a text, including figurative language such as metaphors and similes. **Language 4.** Determine or clarify the meaning of unknown and multiple-meaning words and phrases based on *grade 5 reading and content,* choosing flexibly from a range of strategies. **Language 4.a.** Use context (e.g., cause/effect relationships and comparisons in text) as a clue to the meaning of a word or phrase. **Language 5.c.** Use the relationships between particular words (e.g., synonyms, antonyms, homographs) to better understand each of the words.

Next

6. Part A

Which meaning of the word "vault" is used in the following sentence?

"Many did it because they wanted their turquoise jewelry to be safe in the Trading Post vault until they needed it for ceremonial wear."

- ○ **A.** a jump or leap over something
- ○ **B.** a space with an arched ceiling
- ○ **C.** a place to bury a dead body
- ○ **D.** a place to keep valuable things

Part B

Which words from the passage are the best clue to the meaning of the word?

- ○ **A.** ceremonial wear
- ○ **B.** to be safe
- ○ **C.** needed money
- ○ **D.** in exchange

COMMON CORE STATE STANDARDS

Literature 4. Determine the meaning of words and phrases as they are used in a text, including figurative language such as metaphors and similes. **Language 4.** Determine or clarify the meaning of unknown and multiple-meaning words and phrases based on *grade 5 reading and content,* choosing flexibly from a range of strategies. **Language 4.a.** Use context (e.g., cause/effect relationships and comparisons in text) as a clue to the meaning of a word or phrase.

Next

Name _____

Writing – Constructed Response

Based on the information in the passage from the selection *A Summer's Trade,* write a short dialogue that took place between Tony and Mr. Hilson when Tony got the job at the Trading Post.

Expand on the text by adding your own ideas. Use the dialogue to establish the situation and to show the responses of the characters to each other and to the situation. Reread your dialogue and correct any errors in punctuation, spelling, capitalization, and grammar.

_____

_____

_____

_____

_____

_____

_____

_____

_____

_____

_____

To the Teacher: Use the Writing Rubric on page T17 to assess students' writing.

COMMON CORE STATE STANDARDS

Literature 1. Quote accurately from a text when explaining what the text says explicitly and when drawing inferences from the text. **Writing 3.** Write narratives to develop real or imagined experiences or events using effective technique, descriptive details, and clear event sequence. **Writing 3.a.** Orient the reader by establishing a situation and introducing a narrator and/or characters; organize an event sequence that unfolds naturally. **Writing 3.b.** Use narrative techniques, such as dialogue, description, and pacing, to develop experiences and events or show the responses of characters to situations. **Writing 4.** Produce clear and coherent writing in which the development and organization are appropriate to task, purpose, and audience. **Language 1.** Demonstrate command of the conventions of standard English grammar and usage when writing or speaking. **Language 2.** Demonstrate command of the conventions of standard English capitalization, punctuation, and spelling when writing.

Next

Writing – Extended Response

You have read two texts about characters who make sacrifices for others.

- *A Summer's Trade*
- *The Ch'i-lin Purse*

Despite vast differences in their genres, characters, and settings, these two stories have important similarities in their plots and in the lessons they teach. Write an essay in which you compare the stories' plots and lessons. Introduce the topic and then develop it with facts, details, and examples from the selections. Provide a concluding statement that sums up your main points. Remember to follow the conventions of standard English grammar and use correct capitalization, punctuation, and spelling.

To the Teacher: Tell students they may use the space on this page to plan their writing. Then have them write their response on the following pages. Use the Writing Rubric on page T18 to assess students' writing.

COMMON CORE STATE STANDARDS

Literature 3. Compare and contrast two or more characters, settings, or events in a story or drama, drawing on specific details in the text (e.g., how characters interact). **Writing 2.** Write informative/ explanatory texts to examine a topic and convey ideas and information clearly. **Writing 2.b.** Develop the topic with facts, definitions, concrete details, quotations, or other information and examples related to the topic. **Writing 2.d.** Use precise language and domain-specific vocabulary to inform about or explain the topic. **Writing 2.e.** Provide a concluding statement or section related to the information or explanation presented. **Language 1.** Demonstrate command of the conventions of standard English grammar and usage when writing or speaking. **Language 2.** Demonstrate command of the conventions of standard English capitalization, punctuation, and spelling when writing.

Next

Name _____

_____

_____

_____

_____

_____

_____

_____

_____

_____

_____

_____

_____

_____

_____

_____

_____

_____

_____

_____

_____

_____

_____

_____

_____

_____

_____

_____

_____

_____

_____

_____

_____

_____

_____

_____

_____

Directions: Read the following passage. Use information from the passage to answer the questions.

The Midnight Ride of Paul Revere
by Henry Wadsworth Longfellow

[1]

Listen, my children,

And you shall hear

Of the midnight ride of Paul Revere,

On the eighteenth of April, in Seventy-Five,

Hardly a man is now alive

Who remembers that famous day and year.

[2]

He said to his friend, "If the British march

By land or sea from the town tonight,

Hang a lantern aloft in the belfry arch

Of the North Church tower as a signal light—

One, if by land, and two, if by sea;

And I on the opposite shore will be,

Ready to ride and spread the alarm

Through every Middlesex village and farm,

For the country folk to be up and to arm."

[3]

Then he said, "Good night!"

    and with muffled oar

Silently rowed to the Charlestown shore,

Just as the moon rose over the bay,

Where swinging wide at her moorings lay

The *Somerset,* British man-of-war;

A phantom ship, with each mast and spar

Across the moon like a prison bar,

And a huge black hulk, that was magnified

By its own reflection in the tide.

Next

[4]

Meanwhile, his friend, through alley and street,

Wanders and watches, with eager ears,

Till in the silence around him he hears

The muster of men at the barrack door,

The sound of arms, and the tramp of feet,

And the measured tread of the grenadiers,

Marching down to their boats on the shore.

[5]

Then he climbed the tower

   of the Old North Church,

By the wooden stairs, with stealthy tread,

To the belfry-chamber overhead,

And startled the pigeons from their perch

On the somber rafters, that round him made

Masses and moving shapes of shade—

By the trembling ladder, steep and tall,

To the highest window in the wall,

Where he paused to listen and look down

A moment on the roofs of the town,

And the moonlight flowing over all.

[6]

Beneath in the churchyard, lay the dead,

In their night-encampment on the hill,

Wrapped in silence so deep and still

That he could hear, like a sentinel's tread,

The watchful night-wind, as it went

Creeping along from tent to tent,

And seeming to whisper, "All is well!"

A moment only he feels the spell

Of the place and the hour, the secret dread
Of the lonely belfry and the dead;
For suddenly all his thoughts are bent
On a shadowy something far away,
Where the river widens to meet the bay—
A line of black that bends and floats
On the rising tide, like a bridge of boats.

[7]

Meanwhile, impatient to mount and ride,
Booted and spurred, with a heavy stride
On the opposite shore walked Paul Revere.
Now he patted his horse's side,
Now gazed on the landscape far and near,
Then, impetuous, stamped the earth,
And turned and tightened his saddle girth;
But mostly he watched with eager search
The belfry tower of the Old North Church,
As it rose above the graves on the hill,
Lonely and spectral and somber and still.
And lo! as he looks, on the belfry's height
A glimmer, and then a gleam of light!
He springs to the saddle, the bridle he turns,
But lingers and gazes, till full on his sight
A second lamp in the belfry burns!

Next

Text-Based Comprehension

Directions: Read the questions below and choose the best answer.

1. **Part A**

   What is most likely the author's purpose for writing the last six lines of
   stanza 3?

   ○ **A.** to describe a British warship of the time
   ○ **B.** to let readers know what is coming next
   ○ **C.** to increase the pace of the action
   ○ **D.** to establish a tense, spooky mood

   Part B

   Which phrase from those lines best supports your answer to Part A?

   ○ **A.** "swinging wide"
   ○ **B.** "Across the moon"
   ○ **C.** "huge black hulk"
   ○ **D.** "its own reflection"

COMMON CORE STATE STANDARDS

Literature 1. Quote accurately from a text when explaining what the text says explicitly and when drawing inferences from the text. **Literature 6.** Describe how a narrator's or speaker's point of view influences how events are described.

Next

Name _____

2. **Part A**

Who is the speaker of this poem?

○ **A.** an observer at the time

○ **B.** a person at a later time

○ **C.** Paul Revere's friend

○ **D.** Paul Revere

Part B

Which detail from the poem excerpt did **not** help you identify the speaker in Part A?

○ **A.** "And the measured tread of the grenadiers, / Marching down to their boats on the shore."

○ **B.** "Listen, my children, and you shall hear / Of the midnight ride of Paul Revere, . . ."

○ **C.** "Booted and spurred, with a heavy stride / On the opposite shore walked Paul Revere."

○ **D.** "Meanwhile, his friend, through alley and street, / Wanders and watches, with eager ears, . . ."

COMMON CORE STATE STANDARDS

Literature 1. Quote accurately from a text when explaining what the text says explicitly and when drawing inferences from the text. **Literature 6.** Describe how a narrator's or speaker's point of view influences how events are described.

Next

3. **Part A**

   Which kind of figurative language does the poet use in the following lines of the poem?

   The watchful night-wind, as it went

   Creeping along from tent to tent,

   And seeming to whisper, "All is well!"

   ○ **A.** simile
   ○ **B.** metaphor
   ○ **C.** personification
   ○ **D.** hyperbole

   Part B

   Which words from those lines helped you identify the figurative language in Part A?

   ○ **A.** "as," "went"
   ○ **B.** "watchful," "whisper"
   ○ **C.** "night-wind," "tent"
   ○ **D.** "went," "tent"

COMMON CORE STATE STANDARDS

Literature 4. Determine the meaning of words and phrases as they are used in a text, including figurative language such as metaphors and similes. **Language 5.** Demonstrate understanding of figurative language, word relationships, and nuances in word meanings. **Language 5.a.** Interpret figurative language, including similes and metaphors, in context.

Next

Name _____

Vocabulary

Directions: Read the questions below and choose the best answer.

4. **Part A**

   What does the word "muffled" mean in the phrase "muffled oar" in stanza 3?

   ○ **A.** made with a special blade

   ○ **B.** wrapped to soften or stop sound

   ○ **C.** wrapped to keep warm and dry

   ○ **D.** carved from a certain kind of wood

   Part B

   Which word from the stanza is a clue to the meaning of this word?

   ○ **A.** "silently"

   ○ **B.** "rowed"

   ○ **C.** "shore"

   ○ **D.** "bay"

COMMON CORE STATE STANDARDS

Literature 4. Determine the meaning of words and phrases as they are used in a text, including figurative language such as metaphors and similes. **Language 4.a.** Use context (e.g., cause/effect relationships and comparisons in text) as a clue to the meaning of a word or phrase.

Next

5. **Part A**

Which meaning of the homograph "spell" is used in stanza 6?

- ○ **A.** write a word's letters in order
- ○ **B.** period of time
- ○ **C.** a person's turn at work
- ○ **D.** magic influence

Part B

Which word from the stanza helped you figure out the meaning of the homograph?

- ○ **A.** "moment"
- ○ **B.** "whisper"
- ○ **C.** "feels"
- ○ **D.** "thoughts"

COMMON CORE STATE STANDARDS

Literature 4. Determine the meaning of words and phrases as they are used in a text, including figurative language such as metaphors and similes. **Language 4.a.** Use context (e.g., cause/effect relationships and comparisons in text) as a clue to the meaning of a word or phrase. **Language 5.c.** Use the relationships between particular words (e.g., synonyms, antonyms, homographs) to better understand each of the words.

Next

6. **Part A**

What is the meaning of the word "impetuous" in stanza 7?

◯ **A.** done in a rude way; impolite

◯ **B.** done without excitement; calm

◯ **C.** done with rash energy; hasty

◯ **D.** done in a timid way; hesitant

Part B

Which of Paul Revere's actions in the stanza helped you choose the word meaning in Part A?

◯ **A.** "stamped the earth"

◯ **B.** "patted his horse's side"

◯ **C.** "tightened his saddle girth"

◯ **D.** "gazed on the landscape"

COMMON CORE STATE STANDARDS

Literature 4. Determine the meaning of words and phrases as they are used in a text, including figurative language such as metaphors and similes. **Language 4.a.** Use context (e.g., cause/effect relationships and comparisons in text) as a clue to the meaning of a word or phrase.

Next

Writing – Constructed Response

Based on the information in the excerpt from the poem *The Midnight Ride of Paul Revere,* write a paragraph that explains Paul Revere's friend's job, Paul Revere's job, and the connection between the two. Answer these questions about each man: What was he supposed to do on that April night in 1775? Why?

Introduce the topic and then develop it using details from the text. Group related information in a logical way. Provide a concluding statement that sums up the importance of what the two men were doing. Remember to follow the conventions of standard English grammar and use correct capitalization, punctuation, and spelling.

_____

_____

_____

_____

_____

_____

_____

_____

_____

To the Teacher: Use the Writing Rubric on page T17 to assess students' writing.

COMMON CORE STATE STANDARDS

Literature 1. Quote accurately from a text when explaining what the text says explicitly and when drawing inferences from the text. **Writing 2.** Write informative/explanatory texts to examine a topic and convey ideas and information clearly. **Writing 2.a.** Introduce a topic clearly, provide a general observation and focus, and group related information logically; include formatting (e.g., headings), illustrations, and multimedia when useful to aiding comprehension. **Writing 2.b.** Develop the topic with facts, definitions, concrete details, quotations, or other information and examples related to the topic. **Writing 2.e.** Provide a concluding statement or section related to the information or explanation presented. **Writing 9.** Draw evidence from literary or informational texts to support analysis, reflection, and research. **Language 1.** Demonstrate command of the conventions of standard English grammar and usage when writing or speaking. **Language 2.** Demonstrate command of the conventions of standard English capitalization, punctuation, and spelling when writing.

Next

Writing – Extended Response

You have read two texts that tell about the most famous ride in American history.

- *The Midnight Ride of Paul Revere*
- "The Heroic Paul Revere"

The two selections feature the same characters, events, and themes but are different genres and therefore have different structures. Which selection do you like better? Why? Write a review in which you answer these questions. State your opinion and offer reasons supported by details from the selections. Conclude with a sentence or section that restates your opinion. Remember to follow the conventions of standard English grammar and use correct capitalization, punctuation, and spelling.

To the Teacher: Tell students they may use the space on this page to plan their writing. Then have them write their response on the following page. Use the Writing Rubric on page T18 to assess students' writing.

COMMON CORE STATE STANDARDS

Literature 1. Quote accurately from a text when explaining what the text says explicitly and when drawing inferences from the text. **Writing 1.** Write opinion pieces on topics or texts, supporting a point of view with reasons and information. **Writing 1.a.** Introduce a topic or text clearly, state an opinion, and create an organizational structure in which ideas are logically grouped to support the writer's purpose. **Writing 1.b.** Provide logically ordered reasons that are supported by facts and details. **Writing 1.d.** Provide a concluding statement or section related to the opinion presented. **Writing 4.** Produce clear and coherent writing in which the development and organization are appropriate to task, purpose, and audience. **Language 1.** Demonstrate command of the conventions of standard English grammar and usage when writing or speaking. **Language 2.** Demonstrate command of the conventions of standard English capitalization, punctuation, and spelling when writing.

Next

_____

_____

_____

_____

_____

_____

_____

_____

_____

_____

_____

_____

_____

_____

_____

_____

_____

_____

_____

_____

_____

_____

_____

Name _____

Directions: Read the following passage. Use information from the passage to answer the questions.

The Toy Space Shuttle Is Here!

You've seen the launch of a space shuttle on TV. Now launch one in your backyard!

That's right. The Toy Space Shuttle is an exact replica of a NASA space shuttle. Only it measures just one foot tall and four inches across.

But here's the really big news. The Toy Space Shuttle can do everything that a real space shuttle can do. When you launch the Toy Space Shuttle, it rockets up, up, up into the sky. It keeps soaring until it disappears from sight. That's when you run upstairs to your bedroom. The Toy Space Shuttle comes with its own Mission Control Center, just like the one at the NASA Johnson Space Center in Houston, Texas. It is small enough to fit on your desk, but powerful enough to let you track your Toy Space Shuttle while it is in orbit!

You read that correctly. The Toy Space Shuttle can orbit around the Earth!

How do you play with a toy that is so far away? It's easy.

Put on your Mission Control Center headphones. Key in your password. Now that you've logged in, you can see and hear everything that your Toy Space Shuttle is doing. You can even direct your Toy Space Shuttle to take photos of the Earth. It's truly amazing!

Ever wondered what Iceland looks like? Direct your Toy Space Shuttle to fly above it. Punch in the code to tell your Toy Space Shuttle to take some pictures of Iceland. Then download the photos to your computer. Whatever fun you've ever had in your life, there is no way it compares to this!

It's even better if your friend also has a Toy Space Shuttle. Then, you can view each other's shuttle missions. You can even arrange for your Toy Space Shuttles to meet up in orbit! How cool is that?

When you're ready to have your Toy Space Shuttle come back, simply key in the code for HOME. This tells the Toy Space Shuttle to head on home. You can monitor your shuttle's progress from your Mission Control Center. You can even program the Toy Space Shuttle to fly into your bedroom window. Just be sure to leave your window open!

Here's what one happy customer had to say about the Toy Space Shuttle:

"Ever since I got the Toy Space Shuttle, I have been smiling twenty-four hours a day. I rush home from school in order to check in at Mission Control. Will my shuttle be flying near Asia today? or Australia? I can't wait to find out. Because of the Toy Space Shuttle, I have become really interested in space travel. I think I may want to become an astronaut. And I owe it all to this remarkable invention."

Parents will love the Toy Space Shuttle too. One parent who bought it said, "We used to get our children all these fancy toys, which they would misplace or lose. But with the Toy Space Shuttle, we know exactly where that toy is. All we have to do is look at the Mission Control Center."

There is something wonderful about having a toy that can go into orbit. Every time your Toy Space Shuttle comes home, you can give it a hug. It's pretty amazing to have a toy that has flown so high!

In short, if you want to have fun, if you want to learn about space, if you want to be happy, you should run out and buy the Toy Space Shuttle. It is more exciting than any video game. It is more educational than any book about space travel. It is the invention of the century.

So get your Toy Space Shuttle now before they're all gone! For a special price of just $10,000, you will agree that this fabulous and amazing toy is well worth the money.

Next

Text-Based Comprehension

Directions: Read the questions below and choose the best answer.

1. **Part A**

   What do you do before you are connected to the Mission Control Center?

   ○ **A.** You see what your toy is doing.
   ○ **B.** You key in your password.
   ○ **C.** You view your friends' missions.
   ○ **D.** You arrange to take pictures.

   Part B

   Which phrase from the selection helped you choose the event in Part A?

   ○ **A.** "That's when you run upstairs"
   ○ **B.** "'I rush home from school'"
   ○ **C.** "When you're ready"
   ○ **D.** "Now that you've logged in,"

COMMON CORE STATE STANDARDS

Literature 1. Quote accurately from a text when explaining what the text says explicitly and when drawing inferences from the text.

Next

2. **Part A**

What is the unstated main idea of the third paragraph?

○ **A.** The Toy Space Shuttle acts just like an actual space shuttle.

○ **B.** You can pretend you are in a Mission Control Center.

○ **C.** The Toy Space Shuttle can take you into space.

○ **D.** You can visit Houston, Texas, while you are in your bedroom.

Part B

Which phrase from the paragraph does **not** support this main idea?

○ **A.** "it rockets up, up, up"

○ **B.** "soaring until it disappears"

○ **C.** "you run upstairs to your bedroom"

○ **D.** "its own Mission Control Center"

COMMON CORE STATE STANDARDS

Literature 1. Quote accurately from a text when explaining what the text says explicitly and when drawing inferences from the text. **Literature 2.** Determine a theme of a story, drama, or poem from details in the text, including how characters in a story or drama respond to challenges or how the speaker in a poem reflects upon a topic; summarize the text.

Next

3. **Part A**

What is the main idea of the selection?

○ **A.** The Toy Space Shuttle can take cool pictures.

○ **B.** The Toy Space Shuttle will let you play with your friends.

○ **C.** The Toy Space Shuttle is a wonderful toy.

○ **D.** The Toy Space Shuttle is impossible to lose.

Part B

Which detail from the selection best supports that main idea?

○ **A.** "The Toy Space Shuttle can do everything that a real space shuttle can do."

○ **B.** "Ever wondered what Iceland looks like?"

○ **C.** "It's even better if your friend also has a Toy Space Shuttle."

○ **D.** "Parents will love the Toy Space Shuttle too."

COMMON CORE STATE STANDARDS

Literature 1. Quote accurately from a text when explaining what the text says explicitly and when drawing inferences from the text. **Literature 2.** Determine a theme of a story, drama, or poem from details in the text, including how characters in a story or drama respond to challenges or how the speaker in a poem reflects upon a topic; summarize the text.

Vocabulary

Directions: Read the questions below and choose the best answer.

4. **Part A**

   Which meaning of the word "track" is used in the following sentence?

   "It is small enough to fit on your desk, but powerful enough to let you track your Toy Space Shuttle while it is in orbit!"

   ○ **A.** observe the path of a moving object

   ○ **B.** carry on your feet and leave on the floor

   ○ **C.** use evidence to find a missing person

   ○ **D.** follow grooves in a recording

   Part B

   Which word from the passage is the best clue to the meaning of "track"?

   ○ **A.** "disappears"

   ○ **B.** "launch"

   ○ **C.** "orbit"

   ○ **D.** "powerful"

COMMON CORE STATE STANDARDS

Literature 4. Determine the meaning of words and phrases as they are used in a text, including figurative language such as metaphors and similes. **Language 4.** Determine or clarify the meaning of unknown and multiple-meaning words and phrases based on *grade 5 reading and content,* choosing flexibly from a range of strategies. **Language 4.a.** Use context (e.g., cause/effect relationships and comparisons in text) as a clue to the meaning of a word or phrase.

5. **Part A**

Which word is a synonym for the word "program" in the following sentences?

"You can even program the Toy Space Shuttle to fly into your bedroom window. Just be sure to leave your window open!"

○ **A.** convince

○ **B.** instruct

○ **C.** organize

○ **D.** outline

Part B

In which sentence does the verb offer a clue to the meaning of "program"?

○ **A.** "Direct your Toy Space Shuttle to fly above it."

○ **B.** "Then download the photos to your computer."

○ **C.** "Then, you can view each other's shuttle missions."

○ **D.** "It is more educational than any book about space travel."

COMMON CORE STATE STANDARDS

Literature 4. Determine the meaning of words and phrases as they are used in a text, including figurative language such as metaphors and similes. **Language 4.a.** Use context (e.g., cause/effect relationships and comparisons in text) as a clue to the meaning of a word or phrase. **Language 5.c.** Use the relationship between particular words (e.g., synonyms, antonyms, homographs) to better understand each of the words.

Next

6. **Part A**

What is the meaning of the word "launch" in the following sentence?

"When you launch the Toy Space Shuttle, it rockets up, up, up into the sky."

○ **A.** load into something

○ **B.** sail on the water

○ **C.** walk away quickly

○ **D.** send off forcefully

Part B

Which context clue helped you figure out the meaning?

○ **A.** "it disappears"

○ **B.** "rockets up"

○ **C.** "do everything"

○ **D.** "you run"

COMMON CORE STATE STANDARDS

Literature 4. Determine the meaning of words and phrases as they are used in a text, including figurative language such as metaphors and similes. **Language 4.** Determine or clarify the meaning of unknown and multiple-meaning words and phrases based on *grade 5 reading and content,* choosing flexibly from a range of strategies. **Language 4.a.** Use context (e.g., cause/effect relationships and comparisons in text) as a clue to the meaning of a word or phrase.

Next

Writing – Constructed Response

Based on the information in the selection "The Toy Space Shuttle Is Here!"
write a log entry about the day you buy and try out the Toy Space Shuttle. Tell
what happens.

Organize your imagined events in a clear sequence. Use sensory details and
description to develop the events and experiences and to show your responses to
them. Conclude with a surprise event that follows naturally from earlier events.

_____

_____

_____

_____

_____

_____

_____

_____

_____

_____

_____

_____

To the Teacher: Use the Writing Rubric on page T17 to assess students' writing.

COMMON CORE STATE STANDARDS

Literature 1. Quote accurately from a text when explaining what the text says explicitly and when drawing
inferences from the text. **Writing 3.** Write narratives to develop real or imagined experiences or events
using effective technique, descriptive details, and clear event sequences. **Writing 3.b.** Use narrative
techniques, such as dialogue, description, and pacing, to develop experiences and events or show the
responses of characters to situations. **Writing 3.d.** Use concrete words and phrases and sensory details to
convey experiences and events precisely. **Writing 3.e.** Provide a conclusion that follows from the narrated
experiences or events. **Writing 4.** Produce clear and coherent writing in which the development and
organization are appropriate to task, purpose, and audience.

Next

Writing – Extended Response

You have read two texts about fictional inventions.

- "The Toy Space Shuttle Is Here!"
- *The Fabulous Perpetual Motion Machine*

Imagine that both inventions are real, affordable, and available in any toy store. Write a review in which you describe both and tell which you think is better and why. State your opinion and offer reasons supported by details from the selections as well as your own ideas. Provide a concluding section that restates your opinion and main reasons. Remember to follow the conventions of standard English grammar, capitalization, punctuation, and spelling.

To the Teacher: Tell students they may use the space on this page to plan their writing. Then have them write their response on the following pages. Use the Writing Rubric on page T18 to assess students' writing.

COMMON CORE STATE STANDARDS

Literature 1. Quote accurately from a text when explaining what the text says explicitly and when drawing inferences from the text. **Writing 1.** Write opinion pieces on topics or texts, supporting a point of view with reasons and information. **Writing 1.a.** Introduce a topic or text clearly, state an opinion, and create an organizational structure in which ideas are logically grouped to support the writer's purpose. **Writing 1.b.** Provide logically ordered reasons that are supported by facts and details. **Writing 1.d.** Provide a concluding statement or section related to the opinion presented. **Writing 4.** Produce clear and coherent writing in which the development and organization are appropriate to task, purpose, and audience. **Writing 9.** Draw evidence from literary or informational texts to support analysis, reflection, and research. **Language 1.** Demonstrate command of the conventions of standard English grammar and usage when writing or speaking. **Language 2.** Demonstrate command of the conventions of standard English capitalization, punctuation, and spelling when writing.

Next

Name _____

_____

_____

_____

_____

_____

_____

_____

_____

_____

_____

_____

_____

_____

_____

_____

_____

_____

_____

_____

_____

_____

_____

_____

_____

_____

_____

_____

_____

_____

_____

_____

_____

_____

_____

_____

_____

_____

_____

_____

_____

Directions: Read the following passage. Use information from the passage to answer the questions.

Leonardo's Horse

by Jean Fritz

For a man who liked to ask questions, Leonardo da Vinci was born at the right time—April 15, 1452. Everybody was asking questions then. The age was called the Renaissance, a time of rebirth when people who had forgotten how to be curious became curious again. They were exploring new countries, discovering, inventing, looking at old things in new ways. What was the point, Leonardo asked, in copying what had already been done? He had to bring his own experience into whatever he painted. You wouldn't catch him putting a halo around the head of a saint. How could he? He had never seen a halo.

Leonardo da Vinci turned out to be a famous artist; still, he was not just an artist. He could never be just one thing. He was an engineer, an architect, a musician, a philosopher, an astronomer. Once he fashioned a special kind of flute made of silver in the shape of a horse's head. The ruler of Florence, Lorenzo de' Medici, asked him to deliver it as a gift to the duke of Milan. This was lucky for Leonardo. He had heard that the duke of Milan wanted to honor his father with a bronze horse in front of his palace. And Leonardo wanted to be the one to make it.

This would be his mark on history. Hundreds of years later people would point to the horse. "Leonardo made that," they would say.

So he wrote to the duke, listing all the things that he could do. He could make cannons, lightweight bridges, and covered chariots that couldn't be broken or harmed. On and on he went, but he saved the most important point for the last. He could make a bronze horse. In the end, he didn't send the letter. He simply left for Milan. Never mind that he was in the midst of painting a large religious picture in Florence. Let someone else finish it. He had planned the picture and that was the important part.

Leonardo was thirty years old now, handsome with curly blond hair. The duke gave him the job of working on the horse, but at the same time he was expected to take charge of entertainment in the palace. He had a beautiful singing voice, he could play musical instruments, he could juggle and ask riddles, and he was also asked to stage elaborate plays for special occasions. Whenever he had a chance, he went back to the horse.

He visited the stables, studying how a horse was put together.

He needed to understand everything about his subject. He measured and drew pictures until he knew where all the bones and muscles of a horse were. But you couldn't show all the muscles on a statue, he said, or the horse would look like a bag of turnips. You should show only those muscles the horse was using or getting ready to use.

He visited statues of horses. Many were shown in an amble—left front leg moving at the same time as the left back leg. This was not easy for a horse; he had to be taught to do it. Leonardo saw one horse, however, that he described as free—left front leg and right back leg moving together, in a trot. Moreover, both ears were pointed forward. (Some horses pointed one ear back to hear the rider's orders.)

Leonardo was ready to begin.

Next

Text-Based Comprehension

Directions: Read the questions below and choose the best answer.

1. **Part A**

   What is the main idea of the passage?

   ○ **A.** Leonardo da Vinci often studied horses.

   ○ **B.** Leonardo da Vinci had a beautiful singing voice.

   ○ **C.** Leonardo da Vinci enjoyed working with bronze.

   ○ **D.** Leonardo da Vinci was a very talented person.

   Part B

   Which detail from the passage does **not** support the main idea?

   ○ **A.** "He had to bring his own experience into whatever he painted."

   ○ **B.** "He visited the stables."

   ○ **C.** "He could make a bronze horse."

   ○ **D.** "he knew where all the bones and muscles of a horse were."

COMMON CORE STATE STANDARDS

Informational Text 1. Quote accurately from a text when explaining what the text says explicitly and when drawing inferences from the text. **Informational Text 2.** Determine two or more main ideas of a text and explain how they are supported by key details; summarize the text.

Next

2. **Part A**

How did Leonardo respond to seeing other statues of horses?

- ○ **A.** He decided to visit the stables where the horses lived.
- ○ **B.** He studied the bones and muscles of a horse.
- ○ **C.** He wanted to make his statue out of bronze.
- ○ **D.** He noticed many statues did not look natural.

Part B

Which detail from the passage supports your answer to Part A?

- ○ **A.** "This was not easy for a horse; he had to be taught to do it."
- ○ **B.** "the duke of Milan wanted to honor his father with a bronze horse"
- ○ **C.** "the horse would look like a bag of turnips."
- ○ **D.** "He needed to understand everything about his subject."

COMMON CORE STATE STANDARDS

Informational Text 1. Quote accurately from a text when explaining what the text says explicitly and when drawing inferences from the text. **Informational Text 2.** Determine two or more main ideas of a text and explain how they are supported by key details; summarize the text.

Next

Name _____

3. **Part A**

Which inference can you draw about Leonardo based on the fifth paragraph?

○ A. Being an artist was important to Leonardo.

○ B. Leonardo was also a famous singer and musician.

○ C. Leonardo could have worked as a model.

○ D. Leonardo took pride in being an entertainer.

Part B

Which phrase from the paragraph supports this inference?

○ A. "He had a beautiful singing voice,"

○ B. "he was expected to take charge of entertainment"

○ C. "Whenever he had a chance, he went back to the horse."

○ D. "handsome with curly blond hair."

COMMON CORE STATE STANDARDS

Informational Text 1. Quote accurately from a text when explaining what the text says explicitly and when drawing inferences from the text. **Informational Text 2.** Determine two or more main ideas of a text and explain how they are supported by key details; summarize the text.

Next

Vocabulary

Directions: Read the questions below and choose the best answer.

4. **Part A**

The Greek word "mousikê" comes from a word that describes special beings that inspire arts or sciences. Which word from the passage most likely uses "mousikê" as its root?

○ **A.** measured

○ **B.** midst

○ **C.** muscles

○ **D.** musician

Part B

Which word or phrase from the passage is the best clue to finding the word that uses "mousikê" as its root?

○ **A.** "bones"

○ **B.** "Never mind"

○ **C.** "musical instruments"

○ **D.** "drew pictures"

COMMON CORE STATE STANDARDS

Informational Text 4. Determine the meaning of general academic and domain-specific words and phrases in a text relevant to a *grade 5 topic or subject area.* **Language 4.** Determine or clarify the meaning of unknown and multiple-meaning words and phrases based on *grade 5 reading and content,* choosing flexibly from a range of strategies. **Language 4.a.** Use context (e.g., cause/effect relationships and comparisons in text) as a clue to the meaning of a word or phrase. **Language 4.b.** Use common, grade-appropriate Greek and Latin affixes and roots as clues to the meaning of a word (e.g., *photograph, photosynthesis*).

Next

Name _____

5. Part A

The Latin word "palatium" comes from the location in Rome where the emperors' houses stood. Use this meaning to figure out the meaning of the word "palace" in the second and fifth paragraphs.

○ **A.** horse of a military leader

○ **B.** home of an important person

○ **C.** city where the duke lives

○ **D.** country of Italy

Part B

Which detail from the passage also helped you figure out the meaning of the word?

○ **A.** "a halo around the head of a saint."

○ **B.** "the duke of Milan wanted to honor his father"

○ **C.** "painting a large religious picture in Florence."

○ **D.** "Leonardo saw one horse, however, that he described as free"

COMMON CORE STATE STANDARDS

Informational Text 4. Determine the meaning of general academic and domain-specific words and phrases in a text relevant to a *grade 5 topic or subject area.* **Language 4.** Determine or clarify the meaning of unknown and multiple-meaning words and phrases based on *grade 5 reading and content,* choosing flexibly from a range of strategies. **Language 4.a.** Use context (e.g., cause/effect relationships and comparisons in text) as a clue to the meaning of a word or phrase. **Language 4.b.** Use common, grade-appropriate Greek and Latin affixes and roots as clues to the meaning of a word (e.g., *photograph, photosynthesis*).

Next

6. **Part A**

Which meaning of the word "part" is used in the fourth paragraph?

○ **A.** a piece of a machine

○ **B.** where hair falls on either side of the head

○ **C.** an actor's role in a play or show

○ **D.** one portion of a total amount

Part B

Which detail from the paragraph is the best clue to the meaning of "part"?

○ **A.** "He could make cannons,"

○ **B.** "He had planned the picture"

○ **C.** "couldn't be broken or harmed."

○ **D.** "So he wrote to the duke,"

COMMON CORE STATE STANDARDS

Informational Text 4. Determine the meaning of general academic and domain-specific words and phrases in a text relevant to a *grade 5 topic or subject area*. **Language 4.** Determine or clarify the meaning of unknown and multiple-meaning words and phrases based on *grade 5 reading and content*, choosing flexibly from a range of strategies. **Language 4.a.** Use context (e.g., cause/effect relationships and comparisons in text) as a clue to the meaning of a word or phrase. **Language 5.c.** Use the relationship between particular words (e.g., synonyms, antonyms, homographs) to better understand each of the words.

Next

Writing – Constructed Response

Based on the information in the passage from the selection *Leonardo's Horse,* write a news article about Leonardo and how he is prepared to make a bronze horse.

Introduce the topic and then develop it using details from the text. Group related information in a logical way. Provide a concluding statement that sums up his greatest strength as an artist.

_____

_____

_____

_____

_____

_____

_____

_____

_____

_____

_____

_____

_____

To the Teacher: Use the Writing Rubric on page T17 to assess students' writing.

COMMON CORE STATE STANDARDS

Writing 2. Write informative/explanatory texts to examine a topic and convey ideas and information clearly. **Writing 2.a.** Introduce a topic clearly, provide a general observation and focus, and group related information logically; include formatting (e.g., headings), illustrations, and multimedia when useful to aiding comprehension. **Writing 2.b.** Develop the topic with facts, definitions, concrete details, quotations, or other information and examples related to the topic. **Writing 2.e.** Provide a concluding statement or section related to the information or explanation presented. **Writing 4.** Produce clear and coherent writing in which the development and organization are appropriate to task, purpose, and audience. **Writing 9.** Draw evidence from literary or informational texts to support analysis, reflection, and research.

Next

Writing – Extended Response

You have read two texts about famous artists.

- *Leonardo's Horse*
- "A Job for Michelangelo"

Imagine a conversation between Leonardo and Michelangelo in which they compare their lives as artists. Write their conversation using facts and details from both texts. Establish the situation and use dialogue and description to show how the characters responded to experiences and events. Remember to follow the conventions of standard English grammar, capitalization, punctuation, and spelling.

To the Teacher: Tell students they may use the space on this page to plan their writing. Then have them write their response on the following pages. Use the Writing Rubric on page T18 to assess students' writing.

COMMON CORE STATE STANDARDS

Informational Text 1. Quote accurately from a text when explaining what the text says explicitly and when drawing inferences from the text. **Writing 3.** Write narratives to develop real or imagined experiences or events using effective technique, descriptive details, and clear event sequences. **Writing 3.a.** Orient the reader by establishing a situation and introducing a narrator and/or characters; organize an event sequence that unfolds naturally. **Writing 3.b.** Use narrative techniques, such as dialogue, description, and pacing, to develop experiences and events or show the responses of characters to situations. **Writing 3.d.** Use concrete words and phrases and sensory details to convey experiences and events precisely. **Writing 4.** Produce clear and coherent writing in which the development and organization are appropriate to task, purpose, and audience. **Writing 9.** Draw evidence from literary or informational texts to support analysis, reflection, and research. **Language 1.** Demonstrate command of the conventions of standard English grammar and usage when writing or speaking. **Language 2.** Demonstrate command of the conventions of standard English capitalization, punctuation, and spelling when writing.

Next

Name _____

_____

_____

_____

_____

_____

_____

_____

_____

_____

_____

_____

_____

_____

_____

_____

_____

_____

_____

_____

_____

_____

_____

_____

_____

_____

_____

_____

_____

_____

_____

_____

_____

_____

_____

_____

_____

_____

_____

Name _____

Directions: Read the following passage. Use information from the passage to answer the questions.

The Dinosaurs of Waterhouse Hawkins
by Barbara Kerley

Horse-drawn carriages clattered down the streets of London in 1853. Gentlemen tipped their hats to ladies passing by. Children ducked and dodged on their way to school.

But Benjamin Waterhouse Hawkins had no time to be out and about. Waterhouse, as he liked to call himself, hurried toward his workshop in a park south of town. He was expecting some very important visitors. He didn't want to be late.

As he neared his workshop, Waterhouse thought of the hours he'd spent outside as a boy. Like many artists, he had grown up sketching the world around him. By the time he was a young man, he'd found his true passion: animals. He loved to draw and paint them. But what he really loved was sculpting models of them. Through his care and hard work, they seemed to come to life.

Now Waterhouse was busy with a most exciting project: He was building dinosaurs! His creations would prowl the grounds of Queen Victoria and Prince Albert's new art and science museum, the Crystal Palace.

Even though the English had found the first known dinosaur fossil many years before—and the bones of more dinosaurs had been unearthed in England since then—in 1853, most people had no idea what a dinosaur looked like.

Scientists weren't sure either, for the only fossils were some bits and pieces—a tooth here, a bone there. But they thought that if they studied a fossil and compared it to a living animal, they could fill in the blanks.

And so, with the help of scientist Richard Owen, who checked every muscle, bone, and spike, that's exactly what Waterhouse was doing. He wanted to create such perfect models that anyone—a crowd of curious children, England's leading scientists, even the Queen herself!—could gaze at his dinosaurs and see into the past.

Waterhouse threw open the doors to his workshop. Nervously, he tidied up here and there. His assistants came, then Richard Owen.

At last, the visitors arrived: Queen Victoria and Prince Albert!

The Queen's eyes grew wide in surprise. Waterhouse's creatures were extraordinary! How on earth had he made them?

He was happy to explain: The iguanodon, for instance, had teeth that were quite similar to the teeth of an iguana. The iguanodon, then, must surely have looked like a giant iguana. Waterhouse pointed out that the few iguanodon bones helped determine the model's size and proportion. And another bone—almost a spike—most likely sat on the nose, like a rhino's horn.

Just so for the megalosaurus. Start with its jawbone. Compare it to the anatomy of a lizard. Fill in the blanks. And voilà! A dinosaur more than forty feet long.

Waterhouse was also making ancient reptiles and amphibians. While Richard Owen could imagine their shapes, it took an artist to bring the animals to life.

Designing the creatures was only the first step. There was still the monumental task of building them.

Waterhouse showed his guests the small models he'd made, correct in every detail, from scales on the nose to nails on the toes. With the help of his assistants, he had formed the life-size clay figures and created the molds from them. Then he erected iron skeletons, built brick foundations, and covered the whole thing with cement casts from the dinosaur-shaped molds.

"It is no less," Waterhouse concluded, "than building a house upon four columns."

Next

Text-Based Comprehension

Directions: Read the questions below and choose the best answer.

1. **Part A**

   Which sentence in the passage is an opinion?

   ○ **A.** "Children ducked and dodged on their way to school."
   ○ **B.** "Waterhouse's creatures were extraordinary!"
   ○ **C.** "Start with its jawbone."
   ○ **D.** "Designing the creatures was only the first step."

   Part B

   Which word from the sentence helped you identify it as an opinion?

   ○ **A.** "dodged"
   ○ **B.** "extraordinary"
   ○ **C.** "only"
   ○ **D.** "Start"

COMMON CORE STATE STANDARDS

Informational Text 1. Quote accurately from a text when explaining what the text says explicitly and when drawing inferences from the text. **Informational Text 8.** Explain how an author uses reasons and evidence to support particular points in a text, identifying which reasons and evidence support which point(s).

Next

2. **Part A**

What is the unstated main idea of the following paragraph?

"Designing the creatures was only the first step. There was still the monumental task of building them."

- ○ **A.** Building a large model is a lot of work.
- ○ **B.** A brick foundation is needed to support the weight of a model.
- ○ **C.** Assistants are very important to an artist.
- ○ **D.** Small dinosaur models are very valuable.

Part B

Which word from the paragraph best helped you determine this main idea?

- ○ **A.** "Designing"
- ○ **B.** "creatures"
- ○ **C.** "monumental"
- ○ **D.** "building"

COMMON CORE STATE STANDARDS

Informational Text 1. Quote accurately from a text when explaining what the text says explicitly and when drawing inferences from the text. **Informational Text 2.** Determine two or more main ideas of a text and explain how they are supported by key details; summarize the text.

Next

Name _____

3. **Part A**

What caused Waterhouse to think the iguanodon looked like an iguana?

○ **A.** the bones

○ **B.** the spike

○ **C.** the teeth

○ **D.** The iguanodon actually looked like a rhino.

Part B

Which words from the following sentences support your answer to Part A?

". . . The iguanodon, for instance, had teeth that were quite similar to the teeth of an iguana. The iguanodon, then, must surely have looked like a giant iguana."

○ **A.** "a giant"

○ **B.** "similar to"

○ **C.** "that were"

○ **D.** "for instance"

COMMON CORE STATE STANDARDS

Informational Text 1. Quote accurately from a text when explaining what the text says explicitly and when drawing inferences from the text.

Next

Vocabulary

Directions: Read the questions below and choose the best answer.

4. **Part A**

Which meaning of the homonym "casts" is used in the following sentence?

"Then he erected iron skeletons, built brick foundations, and covered the whole thing with cement casts from the dinosaur-shaped molds."

○ **A.** throws over water

○ **B.** shapes formed by special pans

○ **C.** medical devices for broken bones

○ **D.** actors in movies or plays

Part B

Which words from the passage helped you figure out the meaning of the homonym?

○ **A.** "showed his guests"

○ **B.** "correct in every detail"

○ **C.** "built brick foundations"

○ **D.** "covered the whole thing"

COMMON CORE STATE STANDARDS

Informational Text 4. Determine the meaning of general academic and domain-specific words and phrases in a text relevant to a *grade 5 topic or subject area.* **Language 4.** Determine or clarify the meaning of unknown and multiple-meaning words and phrases based on *grade 5 reading and content,* choosing flexibly from a range of strategies. **Language 4.a.** Use context (e.g., cause/effect relationships and comparisons in text) as a clue to the meaning of a word or phrase. **Language 5.c.** Use the relationship between particular words (e.g., synonyms, antonyms, homographs) to better understand each of the words.

Next

5. Part A

Based on context clues, what is the best definition of the word "passion" in the following sentences?

"By the time he was a young man, he'd found his true passion: animals. He loved to draw and paint them."

○ **A.** interest
○ **B.** dinosaur
○ **C.** anger
○ **D.** photograph

Part B

Which context clue was most helpful in answering Part A?

○ **A.** "models"
○ **B.** "hard work"
○ **C.** "loved"
○ **D.** "workshop"

COMMON CORE STATE STANDARDS

Informational Text 4. Determine the meaning of general academic and domain-specific words and phrases in a text relevant to a *grade 5 topic or subject area*. **Language 4.** Determine or clarify the meaning of unknown and multiple-meaning words and phrases based on *grade 5 reading and content,* choosing flexibly from a range of strategies. **Language 4.a.** Use context (e.g., cause/effect relationships and comparisons in text) as a clue to the meaning of a word or phrase.

Next

6. **Part A**

The Latin word "fossilis" means "gotten by digging." Use this meaning to figure out the meaning of the word "fossil" in the following sentence.

"Even though the English had found the first known dinosaur fossil many years before—and the bones of more dinosaurs had been unearthed in England since then . . ."

- ○ **A.** animal or plant part found in England
- ○ **B.** animal or plant part found living with humans
- ○ **C.** animal or plant part found inside bones
- ○ **D.** animal or plant part found in the ground

Part B

Which phrase from the passage also helped you figure out the meaning of the word?

- ○ **A.** "Even though the English"
- ○ **B.** "many years before"
- ○ **C.** "had been unearthed"
- ○ **D.** "people had no idea"

COMMON CORE STATE STANDARDS

Informational Text 4. Determine the meaning of general academic and domain-specific words and phrases in a text relevant to a *grade 5 topic or subject area*. **Language 4.** Determine or clarify the meaning of unknown and multiple-meaning words and phrases based on *grade 5 reading and content*, choosing flexibly from a range of strategies. **Language 4.a.** Use context (e.g., cause/effect relationships and comparisons in text) as a clue to the meaning of a word or phrase. **Language 4.b.** Use common, grade-appropriate Greek and Latin affixes and roots as clues to the meaning of a word (e.g., *photograph*, *photosynthesis*).

Next

Writing – Constructed Response

Based on the information in the passage from the selection *The Dinosaurs of Waterhouse Hawkins,* imagine you are attending the grand opening of the Crystal Palace. Write a paragraph describing your feelings when seeing Waterhouse's dinosaurs.

Establish the situation and organize your imagined events in a clear sequence. Use sensory details and description to develop the events and experiences and to show your responses to them. Add a concluding statement to summarize your feelings.

_____

_____

_____

_____

_____

_____

_____

_____

_____

_____

_____

_____

To the Teacher: Use the Writing Rubric on page T17 to assess students' writing.

COMMON CORE STATE STANDARDS

Informational Text 1. Quote accurately from a text when explaining what the text says explicitly and when drawing inferences from the text. **Writing 3.** Write narratives to develop real or imagined experiences or events using effective technique, descriptive details, and clear event sequences. **Writing 3.a.** Orient the reader by establishing a situation and introducing a narrator and/or characters; organize an event sequence that unfolds naturally. **Writing 3.b.** Use narrative techniques, such as dialogue, description, and pacing, to develop experiences and events or show the responses of characters to situations. **Writing 3.d.** Use concrete words and phrases and sensory details to convey experiences and events precisely. **Writing 3.e.** Provide a conclusion that follows from the narrated experiences or events. **Writing 4.** Produce clear and coherent writing in which the development and organization are appropriate to task, purpose, and audience. **Writing 9.** Draw evidence from literary or informational texts to support analysis, reflection, and research.

Next

Writing – Extended Response

You have read two texts about artists known for making artistic sculptures
of animals.

- *The Dinosaurs of Waterhouse Hawkins*
- *Leonardo's Horse*

Think about the skills these two men used to make their sculptures. Do you think
artistic skills or scientific skills are more important for making the sculptures? Why?
Write an opinion piece in which you answer these questions. State your opinion
and offer reasons supported by details from the selections. Provide a concluding
sentence that restates your opinion. Remember to follow the conventions of
standard English grammar, capitalization, punctuation, and spelling.

To the Teacher: Tell students they may use the space on this page to plan their writing. Then have them write
their response on the following pages. Use the Writing Rubric on page T18 to assess students' writing.

COMMON CORE STATE STANDARDS

Informational Text 1. Quote accurately from a text when explaining what the text says explicitly and when
drawing inferences from the text. **Writing 1.** Write opinion pieces on topics or texts, supporting a point
of view with reasons and information. **Writing 1.a.** Introduce a topic or text clearly, state an opinion, and
create an organizational structure in which ideas are logically grouped to support the writer's purpose.
Writing 1.b. Provide logically ordered reasons that are supported by facts and details. **Writing 1.d.** Provide
a concluding statement or section related to the opinion presented. **Writing 4.** Produce clear and coherent
writing in which the development and organization are appropriate to task, purpose, and audience.
Writing 9. Draw evidence from literary or informational texts to support analysis, reflection, and research.
Language 1. Demonstrate command of the conventions of standard English grammar and usage
when writing or speaking. **Language 2.** Demonstrate command of the conventions of standard English
capitalization, punctuation, and spelling when writing.

Next

Name _____

_____

_____

_____

_____

_____

_____

_____

_____

_____

_____

_____

_____

_____

_____

_____

_____

_____

_____

_____

Next

Stop

Name _____

Directions: Read the following passage. Use information from the passage to answer the questions.

Mahalia Jackson
by Julius Lester

Mahalia Jackson (1911–1972) was not a blues singer. She sang church songs, gospel, but she knew blues and brought the blues feeling into church music. Other people, like Ray Charles and Aretha Franklin, grew up singing gospel, too, but they took the gospel feeling and put it into the blues. The words in a gospel song and the words in the blues will be different, but both can make you start moaning like you've just bitten into the best fried chicken anybody ever made. So that's why you have to know about Mahalia Jackson. Even if she didn't sing the blues, she learned a lot from listening to blues singers, and blues singers have learned a lot from listening to her sing gospel.

Mahalia grew up in New Orleans, Louisiana, the city where jazz was born and where there is still more good music and good food per block than anyplace in the world. Her father worked on the docks during the day loading bales of cotton on boats, was a barber at night and a preacher on Sundays. When Mahalia was five years old her mother died. Her father took her to live with Mahalia Paul, an aunt who lived nearby and the woman for whom Mahalia Jackson was named. Mahalia never lived with her father again, but she saw him almost every day at his barbershop.

Mahalia grew up loving music, and the person she wanted to sing like was none other than Bessie Smith. But Mahalia's aunt was very religious, and she took Mahalia to church every day. When talking about her childhood, Mahalia said that in her church, "everybody sang and clapped and stomped their feet, sang with their whole bodies! They had the beat, a powerful beat, a rhythm we held on to from slavery days, and [the] music was so strong and expressive, it used to bring the tears to my eyes." It was in church that Mahalia first started singing.

She dropped out of school after the eighth grade and went to work doing people's laundry. Mahalia began hearing stories from relatives and friends about how good life was in Chicago, Illinois. So when she was sixteen, another aunt, Hannah, took her to Chicago to live. Once there, Mahalia joined a gospel group and a church choir while working during the day as a maid in hotels.

Next

It was in Chicago that Mahalia got the chance to see her idol, Bessie Smith, who came to town to put on a show. Years later Mahalia remembered that Bessie "filled the whole place with her voice [and] I never went home until they put us out and closed up for the night."

Mahalia's singing brought her to the attention of Thomas A. Dorsey, who directed a number of gospel choirs in Chicago. Dorsey was the father of gospel music, but earlier in his life he had been the pianist for Ma Rainey, the blues singer Bessie Smith had traveled with. He began taking her to out-of-town churches for concerts and her reputation began to grow almost as fast as you are.

In 1946, Mahalia's first record was released. She would go on to become the most famous gospel singer in the world, and in 1976 she received (posthumously) a Grammy Lifetime Achievement Award. Mahalia was a close friend of Martin Luther King, Jr., and at the March on Washington, he asked her to sing right before he gave his famous "I Have a Dream" speech.

Mahalia Jackson had a big voice, and she could go from a high note to a low one as easily as you put one foot in front of the other. She could hold a note until you thought she should run out of breath, and she could put together a lot of notes in a line of music that would take your breath away. And she did it as easily as a cloud floats across the sky.

Name _____

Text-Based Comprehension

Directions: Read the questions below and choose the best answer.

1. **Part A**

   What is the unstated main idea of the third paragraph?

   ○ **A.** Mahalia always enjoyed singing.

   ○ **B.** Music made Mahalia cry.

   ○ **C.** Church influenced the style of Mahalia's music.

   ○ **D.** Mahalia only went to church because her aunt made her do it.

   Part B

   Which detail from the paragraph supports this main idea?

   ○ **A.** "Mahalia got the chance to see her idol, Bessie Smith,"

   ○ **B.** "Mahalia grew up loving music,"

   ○ **C.** "she learned a lot from listening to blues singers,"

   ○ **D.** "in her church, '. . . music was so strong and expressive,'"

COMMON CORE STATE STANDARDS

Informational Text 1. Quote accurately from a text when explaining what the text says explicitly and when drawing inferences from the text. **Informational Text 2.** Determine two or more main ideas of a text and explain how they are supported by key details; summarize the text.

Next

2. **Part A**

Which inference can you draw about Mahalia's father based on the second paragraph of the passage?

○ **A.** He was a hard worker.

○ **B.** He enjoyed listening to jazz.

○ **C.** He did not love Mahalia.

○ **D.** He was very overweight.

Part B

Which detail from the passage supports this inference?

○ **A.** "Mahalia never lived with her father again,"

○ **B.** "worked on the docks during the day"

○ **C.** "more . . . good food per block"

○ **D.** "the city where jazz was born"

COMMON CORE STATE STANDARDS

Informational Text 1. Quote accurately from a text when explaining what the text says explicitly and when drawing inferences from the text. **Informational Text 3.** Explain the relationships or interactions between two or more individuals, events, ideas, or concepts in a historical, scientific, or technical text based on specific information in the text.

Next

3. **Part A**

What is the relationship between Mahalia and the singer Bessie Smith?

○ **A.** Mahalia wants to be friends with Bessie Smith.

○ **B.** Mahalia wants to attend church with Bessie Smith.

○ **C.** Mahalia wants to sing like Bessie Smith.

○ **D.** Mahalia wants to live with Bessie Smith.

Part B

Which phrase from the passage best supports your answer to Part A?

○ **A.** "Mahalia was a close friend of Martin Luther King, Jr.,"

○ **B.** "Mahalia got the chance to see her idol, Bessie Smith,"

○ **C.** "Mahalia's first record was released."

○ **D.** "Mahalia's aunt was very religious,"

COMMON CORE STATE STANDARDS

Informational Text 1. Quote accurately from a text when explaining what the text says explicitly and when drawing inferences from the text. **Informational Text 3.** Explain the relationships or interactions between two or more individuals, events, ideas, or concepts in a historical, scientific, or technical text based on specific information in the text.

Next

Vocabulary

Directions: Read the questions below and choose the best answer.

4. **Part A**

Which word is an antonym for the word "high" in the last paragraph?

- ○ **A.** "big"
- ○ **B.** "note"
- ○ **C.** "low"
- ○ **D.** "front"

Part B

Which word from the sentence helped you choose the antonym in Part A?

- ○ **A.** "had"
- ○ **B.** "and"
- ○ **C.** "to"
- ○ **D.** "as"

COMMON CORE STATE STANDARDS

Informational Text 4. Determine the meaning of general academic and domain-specific words and phrases in a text relevant to a *grade 5 topic or subject area*. **Language 4.** Determine or clarify the meaning of unknown and multiple-meaning words and phrases based on *grade 5 reading and content,* choosing flexibly from a range of strategies. **Language 4.a.** Use context (e.g., cause/effect relationships and comparisons in text) as a clue to the meaning of a word or phrase. **Language 5.c.** Use the relationship between particular words (e.g., synonyms, antonyms, homographs) to better understand each of the words.

Next

5. **Part A**

The first paragraph from the passage contains figurative language: ". . . make you start moaning like you've just bitten into the best fried chicken anybody ever made." What kind of figurative language is used?

○ **A.** hyperbole

○ **B.** simile

○ **C.** metaphor

○ **D.** personification

Part B

What does the figurative language in Part A mean?

○ **A.** You will be happy.

○ **B.** You will be hungry.

○ **C.** You will be in pain.

○ **D.** You will be a great cook.

COMMON CORE STATE STANDARDS

Informational Text 4. Determine the meaning of general academic and domain-specific words and phrases in a text relevant to a *grade 5 topic or subject area.* **Language 4.** Determine or clarify the meaning of unknown and multiple-meaning words and phrases based on *grade 5 reading and content,* choosing flexibly from a range of strategies. **Language 4.a.** Use context (e.g., cause/effect relationships and comparisons in text) as a clue to the meaning of a word or phrase. **Language 5.a.** Interpret figurative language, including similes and metaphors, in context.

Next

6. Part A

Which meaning of the word "blues" is used in the first paragraph of
the passage?

○ **A.** a style of music

○ **B.** very sad feelings

○ **C.** a military uniform

○ **D.** different shades of the color

Part B

Which word from the paragraph is the best clue to the meaning of "blues"?

○ **A.** "gospel"

○ **B.** "church"

○ **C.** "anybody"

○ **D.** "singer"

COMMON CORE STATE STANDARDS

Informational Text 4. Determine the meaning of general academic and domain-specific words and
phrases in a text relevant to a *grade 5 topic or subject area.* **Language 4.** Determine or clarify the meaning
of unknown and multiple-meaning words and phrases based on *grade 5 reading and content,* choosing
flexibly from a range of strategies. **Language 4.a.** Use context (e.g., cause/effect relationships and
comparisons in text) as a clue to the meaning of a word or phrase.

Next

Writing – Constructed Response

Based on the information in the passage from the selection *Mahalia Jackson,* write a newspaper review about a concert by Mahalia that you attended. Tell whether or not you recommend this concert to others.

State your opinion and support it with reasons. Use your own ideas as well as details from the text. Conclude with a sentence that restates your opinion. Be sure to check your writing for correct spelling, punctuation, and capitalization.

_____

_____

_____

_____

_____

_____

_____

_____

_____

_____

_____

_____

_____

To the Teacher: Use the Writing Rubric on page T17 to assess students' writing.

COMMON CORE STATE STANDARDS

Informational Text 1. Quote accurately from a text when explaining what the text says explicitly and when drawing inferences from the text. **Writing 1.** Write opinion pieces on topics or texts, supporting a point of view with reasons and information. **Writing 1.a.** Introduce a topic or text clearly, state an opinion, and create an organizational structure in which ideas are logically grouped to support the writer's purpose. **Writing 1.b.** Provide logically ordered reasons that are supported by facts and details. **Writing 1.d.** Provide a concluding statement or section related to the opinion presented. **Writing 4.** Produce clear and coherent writing in which the development and organization are appropriate to task, purpose, and audience. **Writing 9.** Draw evidence from literary or informational texts to support analysis, reflection, and research. **Language 2.** Demonstrate command of the conventions of standard English capitalization, punctuation, and spelling when writing.

Next

Writing – Extended Response

You have read two texts about famous people in the arts.

- *Mahalia Jackson*
- *Leonardo's Horse*

Imagine you are a famous person in your favorite field of music, art, or drama. Write a brief story for a time capsule, describing the journey of how you became famous. Use details from both texts to help organize an event sequence. Use sensory details and description to develop the events and experiences in your story. Conclude by stating your most important experience from the story. Remember to follow the conventions of standard English grammar, capitalization, punctuation, and spelling.

To the Teacher: Tell students they may use the space on this page to plan their writing. Then have them write their response on the following pages. Use the Writing Rubric on page T18 to assess students' writing.

COMMON CORE STATE STANDARDS

Informational Text 1. Quote accurately from a text when explaining what the text says explicitly and when drawing inferences from the text. **Writing 3.** Write narratives to develop real or imagined experiences or events using effective technique, descriptive details, and clear event sequences. **Writing 3.a.** Orient the reader by establishing a situation and introducing a narrator and/or characters; organize an event sequence that unfolds naturally. **Writing 3.b.** Use narrative techniques, such as dialogue, description, and pacing, to develop experiences and events or show the responses of characters to situations. **Writing 3.d.** Use concrete words and phrases and sensory details to convey experiences and events precisely. **Writing 3.e.** Provide a conclusion that follows from the narrated experiences or events. **Writing 4.** Produce clear and coherent writing in which the development and organization are appropriate to task, purpose, and audience. **Writing 9.** Draw evidence from literary or informational texts to support analysis, reflection, and research. **Language 1.** Demonstrate command of the conventions of standard English grammar and usage when writing or speaking. **Language 2.** Demonstrate command of the conventions of standard English capitalization, punctuation, and spelling when writing.

Next

Name _____

_____

_____

_____

_____

_____

_____

_____

_____

_____

_____

_____

_____

_____

_____

_____

_____

_____

_____

_____

_____

Directions: Read the following passage. Use information from the passage to answer the questions.

Special Effects in Film and Television
by Jake Hamilton

IN MINIATURE

Special effects (SFX) is the art of making the impossible into a fantastic reality. Special effects has always pushed the boundaries of human imagination. It keeps today's movie and television audiences glued to their seats in starry-eyed wonder.

The art of miniature model-making has always been an important part of special effects in movies. Some movie stories have big, spectacular, action-filled scenes. They may call for fights between dinosaurs, explosions on the Golden Gate Bridge, or an armed force charging through the desert. Movie-makers can save time and money by making models for these scenes. This article tells the story of the building of a miniature landscape for a television show.

1 A General Idea

A special effects team must build a prehistoric world in a workshop. The team's first step is to make a "concept" model of this mini-world. The model will give a general view of what the finished product will look like. [The] model shows that the landscape will include a fallen tree and a circular lake.

2 Getting Larger

The movie-makers study [the] concept model to decide on the size and shape of the finished product. Then they make a larger and more detailed "prototype" model. This gives them a clearer picture of how the finished product will look. The prototype comes in sections that are fitted together like puzzle pieces. The 2 ft × 2 ft (0.6 m × 0.6 m) prototype is fully painted and fitted with bushes and trees. Now the team can work on the final product.

3 Getting Started

The full-size miniature model will be 24 ft × 24 ft (7.2 m × 7.2 m). Building it will take real cooperation among all the SFX team members. The model's base is made of the kind of plastic used in fast food cups and boxes. Model-makers carve the plastic surface to make hills and valleys and rivers and lakes. They use references such as pictures of trees and rocks to guide them. [The] model-makers [use] photographs of a dry riverbed as a guide.

4 Carving It Out

[Next], the model-makers [cut] out the area of the huge circular lake at the heart of the model. They will then add more surface detail and mark out other features in the landscape.

5 Rebuilding

The model is cut into sections so it can be taken on trucks to the television studio. Since the model is so large and detailed, each section is numbered. That way, when the pieces reach the studio they can be reassembled easily.

6 Foaming the Model

At the studio, the model is put back together, and the miniature trees, rocks, and other surface details are all put in place. Then a technician wearing a special protective suit sprays the model. He uses a light foam made from toxic chemicals. The foam gives the surface of the model a smooth, natural look. He also adds bumps and dips to the surface. This makes it look just like a real landscape.

7 In the Studio

Putting the miniature landscape back together takes a great deal of attention to detail. Every last tree, bush, and rock must be exactly in place. A huge painted backdrop of blue sky streaked with clouds has been placed on the far wall. Lights positioned overhead will give the landscape more texture and shadow.

8 Fixing in Place

Model-makers use a special glue to make sure the sections will not come apart. The glue is carefully dried by hand. Technicians use the same kind of blow-dryer people use on their hair. That way they can aim the hot wind just right so it will not disturb any delicate details on the landscape's surface.

Next

Name _____

Text-Based Comprehension

Directions: Read the questions below and choose the best answer.

1. **Part A**

   Which type of graphic would be most helpful to understand Step 1, "A General Idea"?

   ○ **A.** a map of the location used to film scenes from the film
   ○ **B.** a clip from the final film, showing the model scene in use
   ○ **C.** a photo showing the completed concept model
   ○ **D.** a table showing measurements for the concept model

   Part B

   Which detail from the passage supports your answer to Part A?

   ○ **A.** "make a 'concept' model of this mini-world."
   ○ **B.** "a general view of what the finished product will look like."
   ○ **C.** "must build a prehistoric world in a workshop."
   ○ **D.** "the landscape will include a fallen tree and a circular lake."

COMMON CORE STATE STANDARDS

Informational Text 1. Quote accurately from a text when explaining what the text says explicitly and when drawing inferences from the text. **Informational Text 7.** Draw on information from multiple print or digital sources, demonstrating the ability to locate an answer to a question quickly or to solve a problem efficiently.

2. **Part A**

Which event must happen before the full-size miniature model is begun?

○ **A.** A technician sprays the model with a light foam.

○ **B.** A painted backdrop is placed on the far wall.

○ **C.** The painted, prototype model is built.

○ **D.** The parts of the model are numbered.

Part B

What information from passage best helped you sequence the event in Part A?

○ **A.** the word "Next"

○ **B.** the word "Then"

○ **C.** the phrase "The team's first step"

○ **D.** the numbered steps of the passage

Name _____

3. **Part A**

Which is a main theme of this passage?

○ **A.** Things are not always as they appear.

○ **B.** Think big, but dream bigger.

○ **C.** Life is a blank canvas, so paint your best.

○ **D.** Slow and steady wins the race.

Part B

Which sentence from the passage best supports this theme?

○ **A.** "takes a great deal of attention to detail."

○ **B.** "making the impossible into a fantastic reality."

○ **C.** "He also adds bumps and dips to the surface."

○ **D.** "Building it will take real cooperation"

COMMON CORE STATE STANDARDS

Informational Text 1. Quote accurately from a text when explaining what the text says explicitly and when drawing inferences from the text. **Informational Text 2.** Determine two or more main ideas of a text and explain how they are supported by key details; summarize the text.

Vocabulary

Directions: Read the questions below and choose the best answer.

4. **Part A**

   Which word is a synonym for the word "reassembled" in Step 5, "Rebuilding"?

   - ○ **A.** separate
   - ○ **B.** take apart
   - ○ **C.** don't change
   - ○ **D.** build again

   Part B

   Which detail from the paragraph helped you choose the synonym in Part A?

   - ○ **A.** The title of the section is "Rebuilding."
   - ○ **B.** The model is cut so it can be moved.
   - ○ **C.** The model is very large and detailed.
   - ○ **D.** The pieces are taken by truck to the studio.

COMMON CORE STATE STANDARDS

Informational Text 4. Determine the meaning of general academic and domain-specific words and phrases in a text relevant to a *grade 5 topic or subject area.* **Language 4.** Determine or clarify the meaning of unknown and multiple-meaning words and phrases based on *grade 5 reading and content,* choosing flexibly from a range of strategies. **Language 5.c.** Use the relationship between particular words (e.g., synonyms, antonyms, homographs) to better understand each of the words.

Next

5. **Part A**

Based on context clues, what is the best definition of the word "prototype" in Step 2, "Getting Larger"?

○ **A.** the very first

○ **B.** a realistic example

○ **C.** part of the total picture

○ **D.** the final piece

Part B

Which context clue helped you answer Part A?

○ **A.** "fitted together like puzzle pieces."

○ **B.** "Now the team can work"

○ **C.** "decide on the size and shape"

○ **D.** "how the finished product will look."

COMMON CORE STATE STANDARDS

Informational Text 4. Determine the meaning of general academic and domain-specific words and phrases in a text relevant to a *grade 5 topic or subject area.* **Language 4.** Determine or clarify the meaning of unknown and multiple-meaning words and phrases based on *grade 5 reading and content,* choosing flexibly from a range of strategies. **Language 4.a.** Use context (e.g., cause/effect relationships and comparisons in text) as a clue to the meaning of a word or phrase.

Next

6. **Part A**

Which meaning of the word "guide" is used in the following sentence?

"They use references such as pictures of trees and rocks to guide them."

○ **A.** something that provides information

○ **B.** a device that directs motion

○ **C.** a person who leads the way for someone else

○ **D.** a person who explains landmarks to a group

Part B

Which word from Step 3, "Getting Started" is the best clue to the meaning of "guide"?

○ **A.** "model"

○ **B.** "model-makers"

○ **C.** "photographs"

○ **D.** "riverbed"

COMMON CORE STATE STANDARDS

Informational Text 4. Determine the meaning of general academic and domain-specific words and phrases in a text relevant to a *grade 5 topic or subject area.* **Language 4.** Determine or clarify the meaning of unknown and multiple-meaning words and phrases based on *grade 5 reading and content,* choosing flexibly from a range of strategies. **Language 4.a.** Use context (e.g., cause/effect relationships and comparisons in text) as a clue to the meaning of a word or phrase.

Next

Name _____

Writing – Constructed Response

Based on the information in the passage from the selection *Special Effects in Film and Television,* write a short interview with a special effects artist about his or her job.

Organize a question sequence that unfolds naturally. Use dialogue and details from the text to show the responses of the artist and to convey events precisely. Conclude with a summary question that follows logically from the interview.

_____

_____

_____

_____

_____

_____

_____

_____

_____

_____

_____

_____

To the Teacher: Use the Writing Rubric on page T17 to assess students' writing.

COMMON CORE STATE STANDARDS

Informational Text 1. Quote accurately from a text when explaining what the text says explicitly and when drawing inferences from the text. **Writing 3.** Write narratives to develop real or imagined experiences or events using effective technique, descriptive details, and clear event sequences. **Writing 3.a.** Orient the reader by establishing a situation and introducing a narrator and/or characters; organize an event sequence that unfolds naturally. **Writing 3.b.** Use narrative techniques, such as dialogue, description, and pacing, to develop experiences and events or show the responses of characters to situations. **Writing 3.d.** Use concrete words and phrases and sensory details to convey experiences and events precisely. **Writing 3.e.** Provide a conclusion that follows from the narrated experiences or events. **Writing 4.** Produce clear and coherent writing in which the development and organization are appropriate to task, purpose, and audience. **Writing 9.** Draw evidence from literary or informational texts to support analysis, reflection, and research.

Next

Writing – Extended Response

You have read two texts about ways to show things that do not exist.

- *Special Effects in Film and Television*
- *The Dinosaurs of Waterhouse Hawkins*

Compare and contrast the making of the miniature scene in *Special Effects in Film and Television* and the making of the giant dinosaur in *The Dinosaurs of Waterhouse Hawkins.* Write an essay in which you tell how these processes are alike and different. Introduce the topic and then develop it with facts, details, and examples from the selections. Use transitional words such as *instead, likewise, on one hand,* and *in contrast* to compare your ideas. Conclude with a statement that sums up your main points. Remember to follow the conventions of standard English grammar, capitalization, punctuation, and spelling.

To the Teacher: Tell students they may use the space on this page to plan their writing. Then have them write their response on the following pages. Use the Writing Rubric on page T18 to assess students' writing.

COMMON CORE STATE STANDARDS

Writing 2. Write informative/explanatory texts to examine a topic and convey ideas and information clearly. **Writing 2.a.** Introduce a topic clearly, provide a general observation and focus, and group related information logically; include formatting (e.g., headings), illustrations, and multimedia when useful to aiding comprehension. **Writing 2.b.** Develop the topic with facts, definitions, concrete details, quotations, or other information and examples related to the topic. **Writing 2.c.** Link ideas within and across categories of information using words, phrases, and clauses (e.g., *in contrast, especially*). **Writing 2.e.** Provide a concluding statement or section related to the information or explanation presented. **Language 2.** Demonstrate command of the conventions of standard English capitalization, punctuation, and spelling when writing.

Next

Name _____

_____

_____

_____

_____

_____

_____

_____

_____

_____

_____

_____

_____

_____

_____

_____

_____

_____

_____

_____

Next

_____

_____

_____

_____

_____

_____

_____

_____

_____

_____

_____

_____

_____

_____

_____

_____

_____

_____

_____

_____

_____

Directions: Read the following passage. Use information from the passage to answer the questions.

Weslandia
by Paul Fleischman

"Of course he's miserable," moaned Wesley's mother. "He sticks out."

"Like a nose," snapped his father.

Listening through the heating vent, Wesley knew they were right. He was an outcast from the civilization around him.

He alone in his town disliked pizza and soda, alarming his mother and the school nurse. He found professional football stupid. He'd refused to shave half his head, the hairstyle worn by all the other boys, despite his father's bribe of five dollars.

Passing his neighborhood's two styles of housing—garage on the left and garage on the right—Wesley alone dreamed of more exciting forms of shelter. He had no friends, but plenty of tormentors.

Fleeing them was the only sport he was good at.

Each afternoon his mother asked him what he'd learned in school that day.

"That seeds are carried great distances by the wind," he answered on Wednesday.

"That each civilization has its staple food crop," he answered on Thursday.

"That school's over and I should find a good summer project," he answered on Friday.

As always, his father mumbled, "I'm sure you'll use that knowledge often."

Suddenly, Wesley's thoughts shot sparks. His eyes blazed. His father was right! He could actually *use* what he'd learned that week for a summer project that would top all others. He would grow his own staple food crop—and found his own civilization!

The next morning he turned over a plot of ground in his yard. That night a wind blew in from the west. It raced through the trees and set his curtains snapping. Wesley lay awake, listening. His land was being planted.

Five days later the first seedlings appeared.

Next

"You'll have almighty bedlam on your hands if you don't get those weeds out," warned his neighbor.

"Actually, that's my crop," replied Wesley. "In this type of garden there are no weeds."

Following ancient tradition, Wesley's fellow gardeners grew tomatoes, beans, Brussels sprouts, and nothing else. Wesley found it thrilling to open his land to chance, to invite the new and unknown.

The plants shot up past his knees, then his waist. They seemed to be all of the same sort. Wesley couldn't find them in any plant book.

"Are those tomatoes, beans, or Brussels sprouts?" asked Wesley's neighbor.

"None of the above," replied Wesley.

Fruit appeared, yellow at first, then blushing to magenta. Wesley picked one and sliced through the rind to the juicy purple center. He took a bite and found the taste an entrancing blend of peach, strawberry, pumpkin pie, and flavors he had no name for.

Ignoring the shelf of cereals in the kitchen, Wesley took to breakfasting on the fruit. He dried half a rind to serve as a cup, built his own squeezing device, and drank the fruit's juice throughout the day.

Pulling up a plant, he found large tubers on the roots. These he boiled, fried, or roasted on the family barbecue, seasoning them with the plant's highly aromatic leaves.

It was hot work tending his crop. To keep off the sun, Wesley wove himself a hat from strips of the plant's woody bark. His success with the hat inspired him to devise a spinning wheel and loom on which he wove a loose-fitting robe from the stalks' soft inner fibers.

Unlike jeans, which he found scratchy and heavy, the robe was comfortable, reflected the sun, and offered myriad opportunities for pockets. . . .

His domain, home to many such innovations, he named "Weslandia."

Next

Text-Based Comprehension

Directions: Read the questions below and choose the best answer.

1. **Part A**

   Which conclusion can you draw about Wesley based on the passage?

   ○ **A.** Wesley is a careful and traditional gardener.

   ○ **B.** Wesley dislikes his neighbor very much.

   ○ **C.** Wesley is a bad student who gets bad grades.

   ○ **D.** Wesley is very focused on his garden.

   Part B

   Which detail from the passage supports this conclusion?

   ○ **A.** "He found professional football stupid."

   ○ **B.** "'Of course he's miserable,' moaned Wesley's mother."

   ○ **C.** "'None of the above,' replied Wesley."

   ○ **D.** "He would grow his own staple food crop"

COMMON CORE STATE STANDARDS

Literature 1. Quote accurately from a text when explaining what the text says explicitly and when drawing inferences from the text.

Next

2. Part A

Which word best describes Wesley at the beginning of the story?

○ **A.** uncomfortable

○ **B.** worried

○ **C.** friendly

○ **D.** likeable

Part B

Which quotation from the passage best supports your answer to Part A?

○ **A.** "His father was right!"

○ **B.** "He was an outcast"

○ **C.** "'I should find a good summer project,'"

○ **D.** "despite his father's bribe of five dollars."

COMMON CORE STATE STANDARDS

Literature 1. Quote accurately from a text when explaining what the text says explicitly and when drawing inferences from the text.

Next

3. **Part A**

How does Wesley respond to the challenge of his summer project?

◯ **A.** He is stubborn and impatient.

◯ **B.** He is determined and enthusiastic.

◯ **C.** He is traditional and curious.

◯ **D.** He is cautious and fearful.

Part B

Which phrase from the passage does **not** support your answer to Part A?

◯ **A.** "a summer project that would top all others."

◯ **B.** "Wesley found it thrilling to open his land to chance,"

◯ **C.** "'Of course he's miserable,' . . . 'He sticks out.'"

◯ **D.** "His success. . .inspired him to devise a spinning wheel"

COMMON CORE STATE STANDARDS

Literature 1. Quote accurately from a text when explaining what the text says explicitly and when drawing inferences from the text. **Literature 2.** Determine a theme of a story, drama, or poem from details in the text, including how characters in a story or drama respond to challenges or how the speaker in a poem reflects upon a topic; summarize the text.

Next

Vocabulary

Directions: Read the questions below and choose the best answer.

4. **Part A**

Based on context clues from the sentence "These he boiled, fried, or roasted on the family barbecue, seasoning them with the plant's highly aromatic leaves," what does the word "seasoning" mean?

- ○ **A.** making flavorful
- ○ **B.** helping to grow
- ○ **C.** type of plant part
- ○ **D.** type of cooking

Part B

Which word from the sentence best helped you answer Part A?

- ○ **A.** "roasted"
- ○ **B.** "aromatic"
- ○ **C.** "barbecue"
- ○ **D.** "plant's"

COMMON CORE STATE STANDARDS

Literature 4. Determine the meaning of words and phrases as they are used in a text, including figurative language such as metaphors and similes. **Language 4.** Determine or clarify the meaning of unknown and multiple-meaning words and phrases based on *grade 5 reading and content,* choosing flexibly from a range of strategies. **Language 4.a.** Use context (e.g., cause/effect relationships and comparisons in text) as a clue to the meaning of a word or phrase.

Next

Name _____

5. **Part A**

Which meaning of the homograph "plot" is used in the sentence "The next morning he turned over a plot of ground in his yard"?

○ **A.** the main storyline in a book

○ **B.** planning or scheming

○ **C.** a patch of land

○ **D.** marking points on a graph

Part B

Which detail is the best clue to the meaning of the homograph?

○ **A.** Wesley is not comfortable around people.

○ **B.** Wesley is planting a garden in his yard.

○ **C.** Wesley has an unusual idea for a summer project.

○ **D.** Wesley makes a robe from plants.

COMMON CORE STATE STANDARDS

Literature 4. Determine the meaning of words and phrases as they are used in a text, including figurative language such as metaphors and similes. **Language 4.** Determine or clarify the meaning of unknown and multiple-meaning words and phrases based on *grade 5 reading and content,* choosing flexibly from a range of strategies. **Language 4.a.** Use context (e.g., cause/effect relationships and comparisons in text) as a clue to the meaning of a word or phrase. **Language 5.c.** Use the relationship between particular words (e.g., synonyms, antonyms, homographs) to better understand each of the words.

Next

6. **Part A**

What is the meaning of the idiom "shot sparks" in the sentence "Suddenly, Wesley's thoughts shot sparks"?

○ **A.** became very active

○ **B.** felt like he had a fever

○ **C.** started planning carefully

○ **D.** became cloudy with smoke

Part B

Which context clue best helped you figure out the meaning of the idiom?

○ **A.** "plenty of tormentors"

○ **B.** "his father mumbled"

○ **C.** "Suddenly,"

○ **D.** "That night a wind blew in from the west."

COMMON CORE STATE STANDARDS

Literature 4. Determine the meaning of words and phrases as they are used in a text, including figurative language such as metaphors and similes. **Language 4.** Determine or clarify the meaning of unknown and multiple-meaning words and phrases based on *grade 5 reading and content,* choosing flexibly from a range of strategies. **Language 4.a.** Use context (e.g., cause/effect relationships and comparisons in text) as a clue to the meaning of a word or phrase. **Language 5.b.** Recognize and explain the meaning of common idioms, adages, and proverbs.

Next

Writing – Constructed Response

Based on the information in the passage from the selection *Weslandia,*
write a paragraph that tells whether or not you think Wesley chose a good
summer project.

State your opinion and support it with reasons. Use your own ideas as well as
details from the text. Conclude with a sentence that restates your opinion.

_____

_____

_____

_____

_____

_____

_____

_____

_____

_____

_____

To the Teacher: Use the Writing Rubric on page T17 to assess students' writing.

COMMON CORE STATE STANDARDS

Literature 1. Quote accurately from a text when explaining what the text says explicitly and when
drawing inferences from the text. **Writing 1.** Write opinion pieces on topics or texts, supporting a point
of view with reasons and information. **Writing 1.a.** Introduce a topic or text clearly, state an opinion, and
create an organizational structure in which ideas are logically grouped to support the writer's purpose.
Writing 1.b. Provide logically ordered reasons that are supported by facts and details. **Writing 1.d.** Provide
a concluding statement or section related to the opinion presented. **Writing 4.** Produce clear and coherent
writing in which the development and organization are appropriate to task, purpose, and audience.
Writing 9. Draw evidence from literary or informational texts to support analysis, reflection, and research.

Next

Writing – Extended Response

You have read texts about how people sometimes need to be alone.

- *Weslandia*
- "Under the Back Porch," "Keziah"

Imagine that you are Wesley, alone in the garden. Write a poem about being alone from his point of view. The poem may or may not rhyme. Use descriptions and sensory details from the texts to establish the situation, convey experiences, and to show Wesley's responses. Remember to follow the conventions of standard English grammar, capitalization, punctuation, and spelling.

To the Teacher: Tell students they may use the space on this page to plan their writing. Then have them write their response on the following pages. Use the Writing Rubric on page T18 to assess students' writing.

COMMON CORE STATE STANDARDS

Literature 1. Quote accurately from a text when explaining what the text says explicitly and when drawing inferences from the text. **Writing 3.** Write narratives to develop real or imagined experiences or events using effective technique, descriptive details, and clear event sequences. **Writing 3.a.** Orient the reader by establishing a situation and introducing a narrator and/or characters; organize an event sequence that unfolds naturally. **Writing 3.b.** Use narrative techniques, such as dialogue, description, and pacing, to develop experiences and events or show the responses of characters to situations. **Writing 3.d.** Use concrete words and phrases and sensory details to convey experiences and events precisely. **Writing 4.** Produce clear and coherent writing in which the development and organization are appropriate to task, purpose, and audience. **Writing 9.** Draw evidence from literary or informational texts to support analysis, reflection, and research. **Language 1.** Demonstrate command of the conventions of standard English grammar and usage when writing or speaking. **Language 2.** Demonstrate command of the conventions of standard English capitalization, punctuation, and spelling when writing.

Next

Name _____

_____

_____

_____

_____

_____

_____

_____

_____

_____

_____

_____

_____

_____

_____

_____

_____

_____

_____

_____

_____

Next

Name _____

Directions: Read the following passage. Use information from the passage to answer the questions.

Tripping Over the Lunch Lady

by Angela Johnson

Do you know how embarrassing it is to be caught in a locker?

Just ask me.

I'm especially not good with my feet *off* the ground. I was telling Mr. Deimeister just that, about the time I went flying off the trampoline over Tony Friedman's head yesterday and scared him so bad (he wasn't spotting for me but was talking to Gus Jackson about what they were going to do after school) that he choked on some gum he wasn't supposed to have in his mouth.

Right around the time he was having the Heimlich done on him and Gus was screaming to apply direct pressure (luckily we'd just had a first-aid class the period before gym), I realized that what everybody calls me is probably true.

Jinx.

That's how everyone refers to me. My own parents, even.

Mom thinks it's cute. My uncle Jeff began calling me Jinx when I started crawling backward as a baby and getting stuck in boxes, under tables, and even, the story goes, a pair of my dad's boots.

Dad pats me on the head like an old skunky stray and says Uncle Jeff was just like me.

Yeah, right.

Uncle Jeff drives a Porsche and lives in a cabin in the woods with a hot tub.

I'm too uncoordinated to ever drive a car, and I'm pretty sure a hot tub is just a bad accident waiting to happen. I love Uncle Jeff anyway, though. I guess he might have been a jinx back in the day. But hey, he must have grown out of it, which doesn't necessarily mean I will.

Next

I'm never going to be able to keep my feet together and fly perfectly on the trampoline. I'm never going to be able to make a basket without breaking somebody's bones (the doctors did do a good job on Mr. Deimeister's nose, though). I'm never going to run like my sister or kick a soccer ball like my brother without falling, throwing up, or pulling a muscle on me or somebody else. My dad won't even let me use a steak knife. I still have to cut meat with one of those plastic picnic things that sort of look like a knife.

But a while ago everything changed—my whole life, even, because of something I saw on the Folk Arts Channel. A couple days after that, a picture in an album made it feel exactly right.

Yes, ladies and gentlemen, boys and girls, people I've run over, stepped on, and tripped up . . . I am going to be a square dance star.

The dancers on television floated over the floor, arm in arm. They smiled, laughed, and nobody fell into anybody else or sprained anything. They were all so happy and even seemed to really like each other. And then I saw this woman who looked just like my mom. She could have been my mom, she looked so much like her. Then in the middle of a swing around she looked the camera in the eye and smiled at me. Honest, it was as if she looked right at me to say: "You could be me, and look—I can do this."

Wow.

It was a couple of days later when a picture fell out of a photo album I'd just dropped in the fish tank (I rescued everything pretty quick, except now our goldfish hide when I come close to the tank), but there in living color was a picture of my mom arm in arm with this kid with hair way down his back—square dancing.

It was in my genes.

Next

Text-Based Comprehension

Directions: Read the questions below and choose the best answer.

1. **Part A**

   Which words best describe Jinx?

   ○ **A.** clumsy but funny
   ○ **B.** goofy but athletic
   ○ **C.** smart but shy
   ○ **D.** bitter but patient

   Part B

   Which detail from the passage best supports your answer to Part A?

   ○ **A.** "Uncle Jeff . . . lives in a cabin in the woods"
   ○ **B.** "She could have been my mom."
   ○ **C.** "a hot tub is just a bad accident waiting to happen."
   ○ **D.** "nobody fell into anybody else or sprained anything."

COMMON CORE STATE STANDARDS

Literature 1. Quote accurately from a text when explaining what the text says explicitly and when drawing inferences from the text.

2. Part A

What is a main theme of this passage?

○ **A.** Heroes can be scared.

○ **B.** Dream big dreams.

○ **C.** Don't play with fire.

○ **D.** Look before you leap.

Part B

Which sentence from the passage best supports this theme?

○ **A.** "I went flying off the trampoline"

○ **B.** "screaming to apply direct pressure"

○ **C.** "'You could be me, . . . I can do this.'"

○ **D.** "I am going to be a square dance star."

COMMON CORE STATE STANDARDS

Literature 1. Quote accurately from a text when explaining what the text says explicitly and when drawing inferences from the text. **Literature 2.** Determine a theme of a story, drama, or poem from details in the text, including how characters in a story or drama respond to challenges or how the speaker in a poem reflects upon a topic; summarize the text.

Next

3. **Part A**

According to the beginning of the passage, which is a correct sequence of action in a recent gym class?

○ **A.** Jinx and Mr. Deimeister are talking, Gus is screaming, Tony chokes on gum

○ **B.** Gus is screaming, Jinx flies over Tony, Tony is spotting for Jinx

○ **C.** Jinx flies over Tony, Jinx and Mr. Deimeister are talking, Tony starts talking with Gus

○ **D.** Tony starts talking with Gus, Jinx flies over Tony, Tony chokes on gum

Part B

Which detail from the paragraph did **not** help you choose the sequence in Part A?

○ **A.** the word "but"

○ **B.** the phrase "about that time"

○ **C.** the word "off" is in italics

○ **D.** the order of the sentences

COMMON CORE STATE STANDARDS

Literature 1. Quote accurately from a text when explaining what the text says explicitly and when drawing inferences from the text. **Literature 3.** Compare and contrast two or more characters, settings, or events in a story or drama, drawing on specific details in the text (e.g., how characters interact).

Vocabulary

Directions: Read the questions below and choose the best answer.

4. **Part A**

What is the best definition of the term "Folk Arts" near the end of the passage?

○ **A.** art based on national television

○ **B.** art based on local cultures

○ **C.** art based on photographs in a book

○ **D.** art based on fishing and raising fish

Part B

Which context clue from the passage helped you answer Part A?

○ **A.** "The dancers . . . floated over the floor,"

○ **B.** "a picture of my mom . . . with this kid"

○ **C.** "But a while ago everything changed"

○ **D.** "I'd just dropped in the fish tank"

COMMON CORE STATE STANDARDS

Literature 4. Determine the meaning of words and phrases as they are used in a text, including figurative language such as metaphors and similes. **Language 4.** Determine or clarify the meaning of unknown and multiple-meaning words and phrases based on *grade 5 reading and content,* choosing flexibly from a range of strategies. **Language 4.a.** Use context (e.g., cause/effect relationships and comparisons in text) as a clue to the meaning of a word or phrase.

Next

Name _____

5. **Part A**

This sentence near the end of the passage contains a metaphor: "The dancers on television floated over the floor, arm in arm." What does the metaphor mean?

○ **A.** The dancers bobbed up and down, as if in a lifeboat.

○ **B.** The dancers were rising in the air, as if in a balloon.

○ **C.** The dancers moved smoothly across the floor.

○ **D.** The dancers wobbled across the floor.

Part B

Which detail about the selection helped you answer Part A?

○ **A.** The dancers are at ease.

○ **B.** One dancer smiles at the camera.

○ **C.** The dancers are friends.

○ **D.** One dancer looks like Jinx's mother.

COMMON CORE STATE STANDARDS

Literature 4. Determine the meaning of words and phrases as they are used in a text, including figurative language such as metaphors and similes. **Language 4.** Determine or clarify the meaning of unknown and multiple-meaning words and phrases based on *grade 5 reading and content,* choosing flexibly from a range of strategies. **Language 5.a.** Interpret figurative language, including similes and metaphors, in context.

Next

6. **Part A**

What is the meaning of the idiom "in living color" in the following sentence?

". . . but there in living color was a picture of my mom arm in arm with this kid with hair way down his back—square dancing."

○ **A.** in shades of gray and brown

○ **B.** full of movement

○ **C.** as a piece of abstract art

○ **D.** in true-to-life color

Part B

Which context clue helped you figure out the meaning of the idiom?

○ **A.** "this kid with hair way down his back"

○ **B.** "a picture fell out of a photo album"

○ **C.** "It was a couple of days later"

○ **D.** "I rescued everything pretty quick,"

COMMON CORE STATE STANDARDS

Literature 4. Determine the meaning of words and phrases as they are used in a text, including figurative language such as metaphors and similes. **Language 4.** Determine or clarify the meaning of unknown and multiple-meaning words and phrases based on *grade 5 reading and content,* choosing flexibly from a range of strategies. **Language 4.a.** Use context (e.g., cause/effect relationships and comparisons in text) as a clue to the meaning of a word or phrase. **Language 5.b.** Recognize and explain the meaning of common idioms, adages, and proverbs.

Next

Writing – Constructed Response

Based on the information in the passage from the selection *Tripping Over the Lunch Lady,* write a news article for a school newspaper about Jinx and the accidents Jinx causes on a typical Friday.

Introduce the topic and then develop it using details from the text as well as your own examples. Group related information in a logical way. Conclude with a sentence that sums up the article.

_____

_____

_____

_____

_____

_____

_____

_____

_____

_____

_____

_____

_____

_____

To the Teacher: Use the Writing Rubric on page T17 to assess students' writing.

COMMON CORE STATE STANDARDS

Literature 1. Quote accurately from a text when explaining what the text says explicitly and when drawing inferences from the text. **Writing 2.** Write informative/explanatory texts to examine a topic and convey ideas and information clearly. **Writing 2.a.** Introduce a topic clearly, provide a general observation and focus, and group related information logically; include formatting (e.g., headings), illustrations, and multimedia when useful to aiding comprehension. **Writing 2.b.** Develop the topic with facts, definitions, concrete details, quotations, or other information and examples related to the topic. **Writing 2.e.** Provide a concluding statement or section related to the information or explanation presented. **Writing 4.** Produce clear and coherent writing in which the development and organization are appropriate to task, purpose, and audience. **Writing 9.** Draw evidence from literary or informational texts to support analysis, reflection, and research.

Next

Writing – Extended Response

You have read two texts about interesting young people.

- *Tripping Over the Lunch Lady*
- *Weslandia*

Imagine that Jinx and Wesley meet and talk about their difficulties at school and their ideas of the garden project and square dancing. Write their conversation using facts and details from both texts. Establish the situation and introduce the characters. Use dialogue, description, and sensory details to show their responses to experiences and events. Remember to follow the conventions of standard English grammar, capitalization, punctuation, and spelling.

To the Teacher: Tell students they may use the space on this page to plan their writing. Then have them write their response on the following pages. Use the Writing Rubric on page T18 to assess students' writing.

COMMON CORE STATE STANDARDS

Literature 1. Quote accurately from a text when explaining what the text says explicitly and when drawing inferences from the text. **Writing 3.** Write narratives to develop real or imagined experiences or events using effective technique, descriptive details, and clear event sequences. **Writing 3.a.** Orient the reader by establishing a situation and introducing a narrator and/or characters; organize an event sequence that unfolds naturally. **Writing 3.b.** Use narrative techniques, such as dialogue, description, and pacing, to develop experiences and events or show the responses of characters to situations. **Writing 3.d.** Use concrete words and phrases and sensory details to convey experiences and events precisely. **Writing 4.** Produce clear and coherent writing in which the development and organization are appropriate to task, purpose, and audience. **Writing 9.** Draw evidence from literary or informational texts to support analysis, reflection, and research. **Language 1.** Demonstrate command of the conventions of standard English grammar and usage when writing or speaking. **Language 2.** Demonstrate command of the conventions of standard English capitalization, punctuation, and spelling when writing.

Name _____

_____

_____

_____

_____

_____

_____

_____

_____

_____

_____

_____

_____

_____

_____

_____

_____

_____

_____

_____

Directions: Read the following passage. Use information from the passage to answer the questions.

The Art of Mimicry
by Robert Kausal

Many animals know that the best way to prevent becoming a predator's lunch is to appear as dangerous or unappetizing as possible. You may be surprised to learn that there are many animals that specialize in the art of mimicry.

Sticks and Stones

There is a critical difference between animals that use camouflage and animals that mimic. Animals that use camouflage try to "blend in" to their environments to avoid predators. Insects are especially good at this. There are insects that look like sticks, leaves, thorns, pebbles, and even bird droppings!

Animals that mimic model themselves after objects or other animals. Some of nature's best mimics of objects are insects. Many insects have adapted by making themselves look like other objects in their environments. They adapt by mimicking the sounds, movements, or behaviors of things or animals in their environments. Let's take a look at some of these animals that mimic.

A Master of Disguises

In the tropical waters of Indonesia lives the mimic octopus. This creature is a master of disguises. Most octopuses hide among reefs and rocky areas, but the mimic octopus's environment is muddy and sandy. Since places to hide are scarce, the mimic octopus has learned to trick predators into thinking it is another type of fish.

The flatfish is one of the mimic octopus's most successful disguises. The mimic octopus can change its shape and glide along the ocean floor just like a flatfish. Why a flatfish? For most ocean predators, eating a flatfish is like drinking sour milk. It tastes horrible! The amazing mimic octopus can also imitate a poisonous lionfish and a sea snake. Some divers believe the mimic octopus has other disguises as well.

Next

It's a Dog—It's a Plane—No, It's a Lyrebird!

While many animals mimic other animals to fool predators, the male lyrebird of Australia mimics sounds to attract females of the species. This small brown bird clears a space in the forest, spreads its elaborate tail feathers, and begins a concert of sounds that amazes and fools any listener.

Besides mimicking more than twenty different kinds of species, the lyrebird also imitates some unusual sounds. These include a chainsaw, a camera, a crying baby, a dog, a car alarm, and even musical instruments! This bird is like a one-man band!

Having a Hissing Fit

Snakes might look scary enough to you and me, but sometimes even they need a little help to keep enemies away. The hognose snake is a harmless snake found throughout the United States. However, its pattern of irregular dark spots enables the hognose to look like a venomous rattlesnake. When threatened, the hognose mimics the behavior of a rattlesnake. It coils up, hisses loudly, and strikes out at its predator, but this is all for show since the hognose doesn't have fangs or venom.

If acting like a venomous snake doesn't work, the hognose will roll over, stick out its tongue, release a foul smell, and play dead. So don't make the mistake of trying to pick up a dead hognose. It's not sterile!

The Last Resort

Sometimes the animal kingdom must rely on the ultimate survival tactic . . . playing dead. Many animals, such as bats, lizards, spiders, and toads, will play dead to fool their predators. This strategy works well. Many predators don't like to eat dead animals. This could be because there is no thrill in the hunt (or in a toad's case, because the animal's body is covered in mucus).

Next

Text-Based Comprehension

Directions: Read the questions below and choose the best answer.

1. **Part A**

   Which type of graphic would be most helpful to understand "Having a Hissing Fit"?

   ○ **A.** a close-up photo of a hognose snake's fangs
   ○ **B.** a photo of a hognose snake sunning itself
   ○ **C.** a photo of a hognose snake playing dead
   ○ **D.** a photo of a hognose snake coiled up

   Part B

   Which detail from "Having a Hissing Fit" supports your answer to Part A?

   ○ **A.** "The hognose snake is a harmless snake"
   ○ **B.** "If acting like a venomous snake doesn't work,"
   ○ **C.** "the hognose will . . . release a foul smell,"
   ○ **D.** "Snakes might look scary enough to you and me"

COMMON CORE STATE STANDARDS

Informational Text 1. Quote accurately from a text when explaining what the text says explicitly and when drawing inferences from the text.

Next

2. **Part A**

What is one of the author's purposes for writing "Sticks and Stones"?

○ **A.** to describe the different looks of insects

○ **B.** to explain why insects mimic other objects

○ **C.** to contrast camouflage and mimicry

○ **D.** to show why camouflage is best

Part B

Which phrase from "Sticks and Stones" best supports your answer to Part A?

○ **A.** "Let's take a look"

○ **B.** "use camouflage . . . to avoid predators."

○ **C.** "best mimics of objects are insects."

○ **D.** "There is a critical difference"

COMMON CORE STATE STANDARDS

Informational Text 1. Quote accurately from a text when explaining what the text says explicitly and when drawing inferences from the text.

Next

3. **Part A**

What is the unstated main idea of "A Master of Disguises"?

  ○ **A.** The mimic octopus lives where it is unprotected.

  ○ **B.** The mimic octopus imitates different fish.

  ○ **C.** The mimic octopus hides among rocks.

  ○ **D.** The mimic octopus tastes just like a flatfish.

Part B

Which detail from "A Master of Disguises" best supports that main idea?

  ○ **A.** "In the tropical waters of Indonesia"

  ○ **B.** "Most octopuses hide among reefs"

  ○ **C.** "has learned to trick predators"

  ○ **D.** "eating a flatfish . . . tastes horrible!"

COMMON CORE STATE STANDARDS

Informational Text 1. Quote accurately from a text when explaining what the text says explicitly and when drawing inferences from the text. **Informational Text 2.** Determine two or more main ideas of a text and explain how they are supported by key details; summarize the text.

Vocabulary

Directions: Read the questions below and choose the best answer.

4. **Part A**

Which word is a synonym for the word "strategy" in "The Last Resort"?

○ **A.** dance

○ **B.** sleep

○ **C.** reptile

○ **D.** plan

Part B

Which detail in "The Last Resort" helped you choose the synonym in Part A?

○ **A.** "rely on the ultimate survival tactic"

○ **B.** "bats, lizards, spiders, and toads,"

○ **C.** "Many predators don't like to eat"

○ **D.** "there is no thrill in the hunt"

COMMON CORE STATE STANDARDS

Informational Text 4. Determine the meaning of general academic and domain-specific words and phrases in a text relevant to a *grade 5 topic or subject area.* **Language 4.a.** Use context (e.g., cause/effect relationships and comparisons in text) as a clue to the meaning of a word or phrase. **Language 5.c.** Use the relationship between particular words (e.g., synonyms, antonyms, homographs) to better understand each of the words.

Next

5. **Part A**

This sentence from ". . . No, It's a Lyrebird!" contains a simile: "This bird is like a one-man band!" What does the simile mean?

○ **A.** The lyrebird can make only one sound.

○ **B.** The lyrebird plays like a concert band.

○ **C.** The lyrebird can make many different sounds.

○ **D.** The lyrebird carries many musical instruments.

Part B

Which context clue from ". . . No, It's a Lyrebird!" helped you figure out the meaning of the simile?

○ **A.** "to fool predators,"

○ **B.** "amazes and fools"

○ **C.** "some unusual sounds."

○ **D.** "small brown bird"

COMMON CORE STATE STANDARDS

Informational Text 4. Determine the meaning of general academic and domain-specific words and phrases in a text relevant to a *grade 5 topic or subject area*. **Language 4.a.** Use context (e.g., cause/effect relationships and comparisons in text) as a clue to the meaning of a word or phrase. **Language 5.a.** Interpret figurative language, including similes and metaphors, in context.

Next

6. **Part A**

The Greek word "mimikos" means "to have something to do with mimes."
Use this meaning to figure out the best meaning of the word "mimicry."

- ○ **A.** the art of dressing in dark clothes and wearing white makeup
- ○ **B.** the art of pretending by acting like another
- ○ **C.** the art of entertaining by using careful movements
- ○ **D.** the art of imagining that you work with invisible objects

Part B

Which detail from the passage is the best clue to the meaning of the word?

- ○ **A.** "This creature is a master of disguises."
- ○ **B.** "Animals that use camouflage try to 'blend in'"
- ○ **C.** "eating a flatfish is like drinking sour milk."
- ○ **D.** "Many predators don't like to eat dead animals."

COMMON CORE STATE STANDARDS

Informational Text 4. Determine the meaning of general academic and domain-specific words and phrases in a text relevant to a *grade 5 topic or subject area*. **Language 4.a.** Use context (e.g., cause/effect relationships and comparisons in text) as a clue to the meaning of a word or phrase. **Language 4.b.** Use common, grade-appropriate Greek and Latin affixes and roots as clues to the meaning of a word (e.g., *photograph, photosynthesis*).

Next

Name _____

Writing – Constructed Response

Based on the information in the passage from the selection "The Art of Mimicry," write a diary-style entry about an imaginary animal that can mimic in amazing ways. Tell about the day from the animal's point of view.

Establish the situation and introduce the animal. Use description and sensory details to develop events and to show the animal's responses to them. Expand on information in the text by adding your own ideas. Include transitional words and phrases to manage the sequence of events. Provide a concluding statement that summarizes the day.

_____

_____

_____

_____

_____

_____

_____

_____

_____

_____

_____

_____

To the Teacher: Use the Writing Rubric on page T17 to assess students' writing.

COMMON CORE STATE STANDARDS

Writing 3. Write narratives to develop real or imagined experiences or events using effective technique, descriptive details, and clear event sequences. **Writing 3.a.** Orient the reader by establishing a situation and introducing a narrator and/or characters; organize an event sequence that unfolds naturally. **Writing 3.b.** Use narrative techniques, such as dialogue, description, and pacing, to develop experiences and events or show the responses of characters to situations. **Writing 3.c.** Use a variety of transitional words, phrases, and clauses to manage the sequence of events. **Writing 3.d.** Use concrete words and phrases and sensory details to convey experiences and events precisely. **Writing 3.e.** Provide a conclusion that follows from the narrated experiences or events. **Writing 4.** Produce clear and coherent writing in which the development and organization are appropriate to task, purpose, and audience. **Writing 9.** Draw evidence from literary or informational texts to support analysis, reflection, and research.

Next

Writing – Extended Response

You have read two texts about changing how others see you.

- "The Art of Mimicry"
- *Tripping Over the Lunch Lady*

Compare and contrast Jinx in *Tripping Over the Lunch Lady* and the animals in "The Art of Mimicry." Jinx tries to change a reputation for causing accidents through square dancing and animals change their behavior to increase chances of survival. How are Jinx and the animals alike and different? Write an essay in which you compare the methods used by Jinx and the animals. Introduce the topic and then develop it with facts, details, and examples from the passages. Link your ideas for comparisons with words such as *similarly, in the same way, on the other hand,* and *after all.* Provide a concluding statement that sums up your main points. Remember to follow the conventions of standard English grammar, capitalization, punctuation, and spelling.

To the Teacher: Tell students they may use the space on this page to plan their writing. Then have them write their response on the following pages. Use the Writing Rubric on page T18 to assess students' writing.

COMMON CORE STATE STANDARDS

Writing 2. Write informative/explanatory texts to examine a topic and convey ideas and information clearly. **Writing 2.a.** Introduce a topic clearly, provide a general observation and focus, and group related information logically; include formatting (e.g., headings), illustrations, and multimedia when useful to aiding comprehension. **Writing 2.b.** Develop the topic with facts, definitions, concrete details, quotations, or other information and examples related to the topic. **Writing 2.c.** Link ideas within and across categories of information using words, phrases, and clauses (e.g., *in contrast, especially*).
Writing 2.e. Provide a concluding statement or section related to the information or explanation presented. **Writing 9.** Draw evidence from literary or informational texts to support analysis, reflection, and research.
Language 1. Demonstrate command of the conventions of standard English grammar and usage when writing or speaking. **Language 2.** Demonstrate command of the conventions of standard English capitalization, punctuation, and spelling when writing.

Name _____

_____

_____

_____

_____

_____

_____

_____

_____

_____

_____

_____

_____

_____

_____

_____

_____

_____

_____

Next

_____

_____

_____

_____

_____

_____

_____

_____

_____

_____

_____

_____

_____

_____

_____

_____

_____

_____

Directions: Read the following passage. Use information from the passage to answer the questions.

The Stormi Giovanni Club

by Lydia R. Diamond

Characters
Stormi Giovanni Green
Hannah
Joseph
Ajitha
Audience

AJITHA: Are you having a hard time with your locker?

STORMI: We didn't have locks at my old school.

AJITHA: You don't have to lock it. I put tape on the side of mine to keep it open. Like this. *(AJITHA shows STORMI.)*

STORMI: Cool. Hannah, did you find a pen?

HANNAH: I got a couple of interesting ones.

JOSEPH: Hannah collects pens.

HANNAH: I'm looking for the perfect pen.

STORMI: Why?

HANNAH: When I was little my grandpa gave me this old silver fountain pen. I wasn't supposed to take it out of the house, but I did, and I lost it. I keep thinking I'll find something almost as cool. It's my passion.

STORMI: That's cool. I have a friend who collects unicorns.

JOSEPH: Next period is lunch if you want. . . .

STORMI: I have a book. *(STORMI exits.)*

AJITHA: That was audacious. *(pause)* Rude and bold.

HANNAH: She's OK.

JOSEPH: It would be hard to start a new school.

AJITHA: That's no reason to be rude. We were only trying to be hospitable and gregarious.

JOSEPH: I was just trying to be nice. *(They sit at a table in the school cafeteria and begin eating lunch. STORMI enters.)*

STORMI *(to AUDIENCE):* Lunch at a new school is the worst. There's this awful time when you have your tray and you have to figure out where to sit. A book can really help. I sit alone and act like I'm reading. I have to act because it's hard to read in all of that noise. But today my plan didn't work. The cafeteria was packed.

AJITHA: Stormi, you can sit with us.

JOSEPH: What are you reading?

STORMI: *A Wrinkle in Time.*

AJITHA: That book is quite scintillating.

HANNAH: Don't mind her. She likes to use big words. She's not trying to make you feel stupid.

STORMI *(to AJITHA):* Do you write stories? *(AJITHA pulls out a dictionary.)*

AJITHA: I try to learn a new word every day. *(reading from dictionary)* Scintillate: to sparkle, gleam.

JOSEPH: *A Wrinkle in Time* is sparkly?

HANNAH: You can sit here and read if you want to. *(STORMI sits.)*

JOSEPH: I thought I would try out for the play.

HANNAH: If you do, I will too. *(STORMI tries to look like she's reading but is drawn into the conversation.)*

HANNAH: It's *The Wizard of Oz,* right?

STORMI: We did that at my old school. I wanted to be the Lion so badly, but I was too small for the suit. I ended up designing the set.

AJITHA: I could enjoy that.

JOSEPH: I want to be the Scarecrow. *(JOSEPH does a funny scarecrow imitation, with limp knees and wobbly head movements.)*

STORMI *(to AUDIENCE):* Lunch was almost as much fun as listening to David's lame jokes would have been. So, I've been thinking. You know how it is when you hurt your finger? Like maybe the pointing finger on the hand you write with. *(STORMI holds up finger and demonstrates.)* All of a sudden you notice all of these things you do with that finger: It hurts to put on a glove. It hurts to sharpen your pencil. It hurts to tie your shoe. And you think, I sure will be happy when this finger is better. Then one day you notice that it's better. You almost can't remember when it stopped hurting. You just didn't notice. It's the same with moving. You can't know when you will stop missing the last place so much it hurts, but you can't stop tying your shoes either. Hey, that sounds a little philosophical. My father would be proud.

Next

Text-Based Comprehension

Directions: Read the questions below and choose the best answer.

1. **Part A**

   What is a main theme of this passage?

   ○ **A.** "Different" doesn't mean "bad."

   ○ **B.** Reading opens new worlds.

   ○ **C.** Never give up!

   ○ **D.** Always do your best.

   Part B

   Which sentence from the passage best supports this theme?

   ○ **A.** "She likes to use big words."

   ○ **B.** "I'm looking for the perfect pen."

   ○ **C.** "Lunch was almost as much fun"

   ○ **D.** "I have a book."

COMMON CORE STATE STANDARDS

Literature 1. Quote accurately from a text when explaining what the text says explicitly and when drawing inferences from the text. **Literature 2.** Determine a theme of a story, drama, or poem from details in the text, including how characters in a story or drama respond to challenges or how the speaker in a poem reflects upon a topic; summarize the text.

Next

2. **Part A**

   What is the purpose of the dialogue in the passage?

   ○ **A.** to explain why Stormi does not like lunch

   ○ **B.** to show that Stormi is making new friends

   ○ **C.** to explain how Ajitha knows big words

   ○ **D.** to compare the characters Hannah and Joseph

   Part B

   Which sentence from the passage best supports this inference?

   ○ **A.** "My father would be proud."

   ○ **B.** "I sit alone and act like I'm reading."

   ○ **C.** "The cafeteria was packed."

   ○ **D.** "We did that at my old school."

COMMON CORE STATE STANDARDS

Literature 1. Quote accurately from a text when explaining what the text says explicitly and when drawing inferences from the text. **Literature 5.** Explain how a series of chapters, scenes, or stanzas fits together to provide the overall structure of a particular story, drama, or poem.

Next

3. **Part A**

Which words best compare and contrast Stormi's feelings about starting at a new school?

○ **A.** at the beginning, hopeful; at the end, depressed

○ **B.** at the beginning, happy; at the end, upset

○ **C.** at the beginning, angry; at the end, accepting

○ **D.** at the beginning, sad; at the end, confused

Part B

Which sentence from the passage helps support this comparison and contrast?

○ **A.** "I have a friend who collects unicorns."

○ **B.** "Then one day you notice that it's better."

○ **C.** "Do you write stories?"

○ **D.** "I want to be the Scarecrow."

COMMON CORE STATE STANDARDS

Literature 1. Quote accurately from a text when explaining what the text says explicitly and when drawing inferences from the text. **Literature 3.** Compare and contrast two or more characters, settings, or events in a story or drama, drawing on specific details in the text (e.g., how characters interact).

Next

Vocabulary

Directions: Read the questions below and choose the best answer.

4. **Part A**

During the conversation that takes place at Stormi's locker, Ajitha uses the word "audacious." What is the best definition of this word?

○ **A.** happy in school

○ **B.** calm and quiet

○ **C.** overcome with hunger

○ **D.** slightly reckless

Part B

Which context clue from the passage helped you answer Part A?

○ **A.** "I have a book."

○ **B.** "Rude and bold"

○ **C.** "Next period is lunch"

○ **D.** "hard to start a new school."

COMMON CORE STATE STANDARDS

Literature 4. Determine the meaning of words and phrases as they are used in a text, including figurative language such as metaphors and similes. **Language 4.** Determine or clarify the meaning of unknown and multiple-meaning words and phrases based on *grade 5 reading and content,* choosing flexibly from a range of strategies. **Language 4.a.** Use context (e.g., cause/effect relationships and comparisons in text) as a clue to the meaning of a word or phrase.

Next

5. **Part A**

During the conversation that takes place at Stormi's locker, Ajitha uses the word "gregarious." Which word is a synonym for the word "gregarious"?

○ **A.** social

○ **B.** boring

○ **C.** mean

○ **D.** afraid

Part B

Which detail did **not** help you choose the synonym in Part A?

○ **A.** Ajitha thinks hospitable behavior is no reason to be rude.

○ **B.** Ajitha thinks gregarious behavior is no reason to be rude.

○ **C.** Joseph says he was trying to be nice.

○ **D.** Hannah says Stormi is OK.

COMMON CORE STATE STANDARDS

Literature 4. Determine the meaning of words and phrases as they are used in a text, including figurative language such as metaphors and similes. **Language 4.** Determine or clarify the meaning of unknown and multiple-meaning words and phrases based on *grade 5 reading and content,* choosing flexibly from a range of strategies. **Language 4.a.** Use context (e.g., cause/effect relationships and comparisons in text) as a clue to the meaning of a word or phrase. **Language 5.c.** Use the relationship between particular words (e.g., synonyms, antonyms, homographs) to better understand each of the words.

Next

6. **Part A**

Which meaning of the word "lame" is used in Stormi's last comment in the passage?

○ **A.** to cause a limp

○ **B.** weak and not effective

○ **C.** having stiff or sore leg

○ **D.** a thin piece of metal

Part B

Which word from Stormi's last comment in the passage is the best clue to the meaning of "lame"?

○ **A.** "fun"

○ **B.** "Lunch"

○ **C.** "jokes"

○ **D.** "listening"

COMMON CORE STATE STANDARDS

Literature 4. Determine the meaning of words and phrases as they are used in a text, including figurative language such as metaphors and similes. **Language 4.** Determine or clarify the meaning of unknown and multiple-meaning words and phrases based on *grade 5 reading and content,* choosing flexibly from a range of strategies. **Language 4.a.** Use context (e.g., cause/effect relationships and comparisons in text) as a clue to the meaning of a word or phrase. **Language 5.c.** Use the relationship between particular words (e.g., synonyms, antonyms, homographs) to better understand each of the words.

Next

Name _____

Writing – Constructed Response

Based on the information in the passage from the selection *The Stormi Giovanni Club,* write a paragraph that describes Stormi's lunch with Ajitha, Hannah, and Joseph.

Introduce the topic and then develop it using details from the text. Conclude with a sentence that sums up the description.

_____

_____

_____

_____

_____

_____

_____

_____

_____

_____

To the Teacher: Use the Writing Rubric on page T17 to assess students' writing.

COMMON CORE STATE STANDARDS

Literature 1. Quote accurately from a text when explaining what the text says explicitly and when drawing inferences from the text. **Writing 2.** Write informative/explanatory texts to examine a topic and convey ideas and information clearly. **Writing 2.a.** Introduce a topic clearly, provide a general observation and focus, and group related information logically; include formatting (e.g., headings), illustrations, and multimedia when useful to aiding comprehension. **Writing 2.b.** Develop the topic with facts, definitions, concrete details, quotations, or other information and examples related to the topic. **Writing 2.e.** Provide a concluding statement or section related to the information or explanation presented. **Writing 4.** Produce clear and coherent writing in which the development and organization are appropriate to task, purpose, and audience. **Writing 9.** Draw evidence from literary or informational texts to support analysis, reflection, and research.

Next

Writing – Extended Response

You have read two texts about students who feel like they are alone.

- *The Stormi Giovanni Club*
- *Weslandia*

If you shut other people out of your life, your feelings cannot be hurt.

Do you agree with this statement? Why or why not? Write an opinion essay in which you discuss this idea. State your opinion and support it with two or more reasons. Use your own ideas as well as details and examples from the texts. Provide a concluding sentence that restates your opinion. Remember to follow the conventions of standard English grammar, capitalization, punctuation, and spelling.

To the Teacher: Tell students they may use the space on this page to plan their writing. Then have them write their response on the following pages. Use the Writing Rubric on page T18 to assess students' writing.

COMMON CORE STATE STANDARDS

Literature 1. Quote accurately from a text when explaining what the text says explicitly and when drawing inferences from the text. **Writing 1.** Write opinion pieces on topics or texts, supporting a point of view with reasons and information. **Writing 1.a.** Introduce a topic or text clearly, state an opinion, and create an organizational structure in which ideas are logically grouped to support the writer's purpose. **Writing 1.b.** Provide logically ordered reasons that are supported by facts and details. **Writing 1.d.** Provide a concluding statement or section related to the opinion presented. **Writing 4.** Produce clear and coherent writing in which the development and organization are appropriate to task, purpose, and audience. **Writing 9.** Draw evidence from literary or informational texts to support analysis, reflection, and research. **Language 1.** Demonstrate command of the conventions of standard English grammar and usage when writing or speaking. **Language 2.** Demonstrate command of the conventions of standard English capitalization, punctuation, and spelling when writing.

Next

Name _____

_____

_____

_____

_____

_____

_____

_____

_____

_____

_____

_____

_____

_____

_____

_____

_____

_____

_____

_____

_____

Directions: Read the following passage. Use information from the passage to answer the questions.

The Gymnast

by Gary Soto

For three days of my eleventh summer I listened to my mother yap about my cousin, Isaac, who was taking gymnastics. She was proud of him, she said one evening at the stove as she pounded a round steak into carne asada and crushed a heap of beans into refritos. I was jealous because I had watched my share of *Wide World of Sports* and knew that people admired an athlete who could somersault without hurting himself. I pushed aside my solitary game of Chinese checkers and spent a few minutes rolling around the backyard until I was dizzy and itchy with grass.

That Saturday, I went to Isaac's house where I ate plums and sat under an aluminum arbor watching my cousin, dressed in gymnastic shorts and top, do spindly cartwheels and back flips in his backyard while he instructed, "This is the correct way." He breathed in the grassy air, leaped, and came up smiling the straightest teeth in the world.

I followed him to the front lawn. When a car passed he did a back flip and looked out the side of his eyes to see if any of the passengers were looking. Some pointed while others looked ahead dully at the road.

My cousin was a show-off, but I figured he was allowed the limelight before one appreciative dog who had come over to look. I envied him and his cloth gymnast shoes. I liked the way they looked, slim, black, and cool. They seemed special, something I could never slip onto my feet.

I ate the plums and watched him until he was sweaty and out of breath. When he was finished, I begged him to let me wear his cloth shoes. Drops of sweat fell at his feet. He looked at me with disdain, ran a yellow towel across his face, and patted his neck dry. He tore the white tape from his wrists—I liked the tape as well and tried to paste it around my wrists. He washed off his hands. I asked him about the white powder, and he said it kept his hands dry. I asked him why he needed dry hands to do cartwheels and back flips. He said that all gymnasts kept their hands dry, then drank from a bottle of greenish water he said was filled with nutrients.

Next

I asked him again if I could wear his shoes. He slipped them off and said, "OK, just for a while." The shoes were loose, but I liked them. I went to the front yard with my wrists dripping tape and my hands white as gloves. I smiled slyly and thought I looked neat. But when I did a cartwheel, the shoes flew off, along with the tape, and my cousin yelled and stomped the grass.

I was glad to get home. I was jealous and miserable, but the next day I found a pair of old vinyl slippers in the closet that were sort of like gymnastic shoes. I pushed my feet into them, tugging and wincing because they were too small. I took a few steps, admiring my feet, which looked like bloated water balloons, and went outside to do cartwheels on the front lawn. A friend skidded to a stop on his bike, one cheek fat with sunflower seeds. His mouth churned to a stop. He asked why I was wearing slippers on a hot day. I made a face at him and said that they were shoes, not slippers. He watched me do cartwheels for a while, then rode away doing a wheelie.

Name _____

Text-Based Comprehension

Directions: Read the questions below and choose the best answer.

1. **Part A**

Which can be inferred about the narrator as he watches Isaac practice gymnastics in the backyard?

   - ○ **A.** The narrator is good at gymnastics.
   - ○ **B.** The narrator does not like Isaac's gymnastics clothes.
   - ○ **C.** The narrator wants to learn gymnastics.
   - ○ **D.** The narrator does not like the taste of the nutrient water.

   Part B

   Which detail from the passage supports this inference?

   - ○ **A.** "watching my cousin, . . . while he instructed,"
   - ○ **B.** "greenish water he said was filled with nutrients"
   - ○ **C.** "listened to my mother yap about my cousin,"
   - ○ **D.** "then rode away doing a wheelie."

COMMON CORE STATE STANDARDS

Informational Text 1. Quote accurately from a text when explaining what the text says explicitly and when drawing inferences from the text. **Informational Text 2.** Determine two or more main ideas of a text and explain how they are supported by key details; summarize the text.

Next

2. **Part A**

Which best compares and contrasts Isaac's behavior in the backyard and on the front lawn?

○ **A.** Isaac eats plums in backyard; he drinks nutrient water in the front yard.

○ **B.** Isaac teaches gymnastics in the backyard; he shows off his skills in the front yard.

○ **C.** Isaac does not do back flips in the backyard; he does do back flips in the front yard.

○ **D.** Isaac does difficult stunts in the backyard; he does easy stunts in the front yard.

Part B

Which detail from the passage helps support this word choice?

○ **A.** "My cousin was a show-off,"

○ **B.** "'This is the correct way.'"

○ **C.** "When a car passed he did a back flip"

○ **D.** "I ate plums and sat under an aluminum arbor"

COMMON CORE STATE STANDARDS

Informational Text 1. Quote accurately from a text when explaining what the text says explicitly and when drawing inferences from the text. **Informational Text 3.** Explain the relationships or interactions between two or more individuals, events, ideas, or concepts in a historical, scientific, or technical text based on specific information in the text.

Next

Name _____

3. **Part A**

What was the effect of the narrator putting on the vinyl slippers?

○ **A.** His skin pushes out of the slippers.

○ **B.** He can do gymnastics better.

○ **C.** He is mistaken for a gymnast.

○ **D.** He finds they fit better than Isaac's shoes.

Part B

Which detail from the passage supports your answer to Part A?

○ **A.** "went outside to do cartwheels"

○ **B.** "I took a few steps, admiring my feet,"

○ **C.** "sort of like gymnastic shoes."

○ **D.** "looked like bloated water balloons,"

COMMON CORE STATE STANDARDS

Informational Text 1. Quote accurately from a text when explaining what the text says explicitly and when drawing inferences from the text. **Informational Text 2.** Determine two or more main ideas of a text and explain how they are supported by key details; summarize the text. **Informational Text 3.** Explain the relationships or interactions between two or more individuals, events, ideas, or concepts in a historical, scientific, or technical text based on specific information in the text.

Next

Vocabulary

Directions: Read the questions below and choose the best answer.

4. **Part A**

The Latin word "supra" means "over." The Latin word "saltus" means "leap." Use these meanings, as well as context clues, to figure out the meaning of the word "somersault" in the first paragraph.

○ **A.** a person who watches over someone who is leaping

○ **B.** a person who leaps in the air when a contest is over

○ **C.** a stunt in which a person tumbles feet over head

○ **D.** a stunt in which a person leaps over a ditch or hole

Part B

Which detail helped you figure out the meaning of the word?

○ **A.** The narrator plays a solitary game of Chinese checkers.

○ **B.** The passage mentions several gymnastic stunts.

○ **C.** The passage describes the narrator's cousin yelling and stomping.

○ **D.** The passage explains that the narrator is jealous of his cousin.

COMMON CORE STATE STANDARDS

Informational Text 4. Determine the meaning of general academic and domain-specific words and phrases in a text relevant to a *grade 5 topic or subject area.* **Language 4.** Determine or clarify the meaning of unknown and multiple-meaning words and phrases based on *grade 5 reading and content,* choosing flexibly from a range of strategies. **Language 4.a.** Use context (e.g., cause/effect relationships and comparisons in text) as a clue to the meaning of a word or phrase. **Language 4.b.** Use common, grade-appropriate Greek and Latin affixes and roots as clues to the meaning of a word (e.g., *photograph, photosynthesis*).

Next

5. **Part A**

Based on context clues in the passage, what is does the word "limelight" in the fourth paragraph mean?

- ○ **A.** a type of dog
- ○ **B.** a type of gymnastic shoe
- ○ **C.** a light in the shape of a lime
- ○ **D.** a center of attention

Part B

Which context clue helped you answer Part A?

- ○ **A.** "dog who had come over to look."
- ○ **B.** "his cloth gymnast shoes"
- ○ **C.** "I liked the way they looked,"
- ○ **D.** "They seemed special,"

COMMON CORE STATE STANDARDS

Informational Text 4. Determine the meaning of general academic and domain-specific words and phrases in a text relevant to a *grade 5 topic or subject area.* **Language 4.** Determine or clarify the meaning of unknown and multiple-meaning words and phrases based on *grade 5 reading and content,* choosing flexibly from a range of strategies. **Language 4.a.** Use context (e.g., cause/effect relationships and comparisons in text) as a clue to the meaning of a word or phrase.

6. Part A

Which word from the passage is a synonym for the phrase "was jealous"?

○ **A.** "envied"

○ **B.** "liked"

○ **C.** "begged"

○ **D.** "admired"

Part B

Which detail helped you choose the synonym in Part A?

○ **A.** The narrator is a good Chinese checkers player.

○ **B.** The narrator enjoys watching *Wide World of Sports*.

○ **C.** The narrator wishes to become a great gymnast.

○ **D.** The narrator thinks he looks good as a gymnast.

COMMON CORE STATE STANDARDS

Informational Text 4. Determine the meaning of general academic and domain-specific words and phrases in a text relevant to a *grade 5 topic or subject area*. **Language 4.a.** Use context (e.g., cause/effect relationships and comparisons in text) as a clue to the meaning of a word or phrase. **Language 5.c.** Use the relationship between particular words (e.g., synonyms, antonyms, homographs) to better understand each of the words.

Next

Writing – Constructed Response

Based on the information in the passage from the selection *The Gymnast,* write a paragraph about the narrator's dedication to looking like a gymnast. He thinks it is important to look like a gymnast in order to be a gymnast. Do you agree or disagree with this view? Why?

State your opinion and support it with reasons. Use your own ideas as well as details from the text. Conclude with a sentence that restates your opinion.

_____

_____

_____

_____

_____

_____

_____

_____

_____

_____

_____

_____

_____

To the Teacher: Use the Writing Rubric on page T17 to assess students' writing.

COMMON CORE STATE STANDARDS

Informational Text 1. Quote accurately from a text when explaining what the text says explicitly and when drawing inferences from the text. **Writing 1.** Write opinion pieces on topics or texts, supporting a point of view with reasons and information. **Writing 1.a.** Introduce a topic or text clearly, state an opinion, and create an organizational structure in which ideas are logically grouped to support the writer's purpose. **Writing 1.b.** Provide logically ordered reasons that are supported by facts and details. **Writing 1.d.** Provide a concluding statement or section related to the opinion presented. **Writing 4.** Produce clear and coherent writing in which the development and organization are appropriate to task, purpose, and audience. **Writing 9.** Draw evidence from literary or informational texts to support analysis, reflection, and research.

Next

Writing – Extended Response

You have read two texts about young people who wish to do well in a sport, but face setbacks along the way.

- *The Gymnast*
- *Tripping Over the Lunch Lady*

Imagine that Gary, the hopeful narrator and gymnast in *The Gymnast,* meets Jinx, the hopeful square dancer in *Tripping Over the Lunch Lady.* They talk about their dreams, plans, and challenges in achieving their goals. Write the dialogue between Gary and Jinx using facts and details from both texts. Establish the situation and introduce the characters. Use dialogue and description to show how they responded to their experiences. Provide concluding dialogue that outlines their future plans and goals. Remember to follow the conventions of standard English grammar, capitalization, punctuation, and spelling.

To the Teacher: Tell students they may use the space on this page to plan their writing. Then have them write their response on the following pages. Use the Writing Rubric on page T18 to assess students' writing.

COMMON CORE STATE STANDARDS

Informational Text 1. Quote accurately from a text when explaining what the text says explicitly and when drawing inferences from the text. **Writing 3.** Write narratives to develop real or imagined experiences or events using effective technique, descriptive details, and clear event sequences. **Writing 3.a.** Orient the reader by establishing a situation and introducing a narrator and/or characters; organize an event sequence that unfolds naturally. **Writing 3.b.** Use narrative techniques, such as dialogue, description, and pacing, to develop experiences and events or show the responses of characters to situations. **Writing 3.d.** Use concrete words and phrases and sensory details to convey experiences and events precisely. **Writing 3.e.** Provide a conclusion that follows from the narrated experiences or events. **Writing 4.** Produce clear and coherent writing in which the development and organization are appropriate to task, purpose, and audience. **Writing 9.** Draw evidence from literary or informational texts to support analysis, reflection, and research. **Language 1.** Demonstrate command of the conventions of standard English grammar and usage when writing or speaking. **Language 2.** Demonstrate command of the conventions of standard English capitalization, punctuation, and spelling when writing.

Next

Name _____

_____

_____

_____

_____

_____

_____

_____

_____

_____

_____

_____

_____

_____

_____

_____

_____

_____

_____

_____

Next

_____

_____

_____

_____

_____

_____

_____

_____

_____

_____

_____

_____

_____

_____

_____

_____

_____

_____

Name _____

Directions: Read the following passage. Use information from the passage to answer the questions.

The Skunk Ladder
by Patrick F. McManus

Early the next morning, Eddie and I headed for the big hole, prepared to start the tedious task of undigging it. As we approached the excavation, a familiar odor reached our nostrils.

"Must be a skunk around here someplace," Eddie said.

"Maybe it's in the hole," I said.

"Couldn't be. We covered it with the door."

Nevertheless, the skunk was in the hole. He had apparently found an open space under the door, slipped in for a look around, and plummeted the eight feet or more to the bottom of the hole. Oddly, he did not seem to be frightened of us. Even stranger, for we did not know that skunks were great diggers, he had hollowed out a huge cavern under one side, in an attempt to dig his way out of the hole.

"We can't fill in the hole with the skunk in there," I said. "How are we going to get him out?"

"Maybe one of us could drop down in the hole, grab him real quick before he sprays, and then throw him out," Eddie said. "I'll yell real loud so he'll look at me and won't notice when you jump in and grab him and . . ."

"I don't like that idea," I said. "Think of something else."

"I got it!" Eddie exclaimed, snapping his fingers. "We'll go up to my dad's shop and build a ladder. Then we'll stick it down the hole and hide someplace while he climbs the ladder. A skunk should be able to figure out how to climb a ladder."

Eddie and I were working on the ladder when his father walked into the shop. "I thought I told you not to build anything," he growled. "What's that?"

"Just a skunk ladder," Crazy Eddie said.

"Oh," his father said. "Well, don't build nothin' else unless you tell me first."

Eddie and I went back out to the hole and stuck the ladder in it. The skunk showed no inclination to climb it, choosing instead to hide in the cavern it had hollowed out. Just then we heard Eddie's father yelling at us: "What did you mean, *skunk ladder?*" We peeked out around the stump pile, and there was Mr. Muldoon striding across the pasture toward us.

"Quick," said Eddie. "Help me put the door back over the hole!"

We threw the door over the hole, neatly hiding it from view. Before we could think of a good explanation for a big pile of dirt out in a corner of the pasture, Mr. Muldoon charged up.

"Now what?" he cried. "Where did that dirt come from? What's my door doing out here?"

He reached down and grabbed the edge of the door.

"Stop, Pa, don't!" Eddie yelled, rushing forward.

From that point on, the actions of the parties involved all blurred together. It is difficult to recall the exact sequence of action, but I will try.

Mr. Muldoon grabbed the door and flipped it off the hole. Then he said, "Smells like a skun . . . " at which time he shot out of sight, leaving his straw hat suspended in the air for perhaps a quarter of a second. (Later, I deduced that Mr. Muldoon had stepped on the edge of the hole, beneath which the skunk had hollowed out its cavern.) A cloud of dust puffed up out of the hole when Mr. Muldoon hit the bottom. . . .

Next

Name _____

Text-Based Comprehension

Directions: Read the questions below and choose the best answer.

1. **Part A**

   Which was a result of building the skunk ladder?

   ○ **A.** The narrator uses it to climb into the hole.

   ○ **B.** Eddie's father uses it to climb into the hole.

   ○ **C.** The friends get in trouble with Eddie's father.

   ○ **D.** The skunk uses the ladder to escape from the hole.

   Part B

   Which sentence from the passage supports your answer to Part A?

   ○ **A.** "'Then we'll stick it down the hole'"

   ○ **B.** "'A skunk should . . . figure out how to climb a ladder.'"

   ○ **C.** "Just then we heard Eddie's father yelling at us"

   ○ **D.** "I deduced that Mr. Muldoon had stepped on the edge of the hole,"

COMMON CORE STATE STANDARDS

Literature 1. Quote accurately from a text when explaining what the text says explicitly and when drawing inferences from the text. **Literature 2.** Determine a theme of a story, drama, or poem from details in the text, including how characters in a story or drama respond to challenges or how the speaker in a poem reflects upon a topic; summarize the text. **Literature 3.** Compare and contrast two or more characters, settings, or events in a story or drama, drawing on specific details in the text (e.g., how characters interact).

Next

2. **Part A**

How does the narrator respond to the challenge of finding the skunk in the hole?

○ **A.** The narrator is courageous and stubborn.

○ **B.** The narrator is fearful and determined.

○ **C.** The narrator is imaginative and cruel.

○ **D.** The narrator is thoughtful and kind.

Part B

Which statement from the passage best supports your answer to Part A?

○ **A.** "'Maybe it's in the hole,'"

○ **B.** "'Think of something else.'"

○ **C.** "'We can't fill in the hole with the skunk in there,'"

○ **D.** "'I don't like that idea,'"

COMMON CORE STATE STANDARDS

Literature 1. Quote accurately from a text when explaining what the text says explicitly and when drawing inferences from the text. **Literature 2.** Determine a theme of a story, drama, or poem from details in the text, including how characters in a story or drama respond to challenges or how the speaker in a poem reflects upon a topic; summarize the text.

Next

3. **Part A**

Which character trait does the narrator reveal in the passage?

○ **A.** his annoyance of events that do not go as planned

○ **B.** his willingness to follow Eddie's lead

○ **C.** his confidence in telling adventure stories

○ **D.** his enthusiasm for inventing and building

Part B

Which detail from the passage supports your answer to Part A?

○ **A.** "Eddie and I were working on the ladder"

○ **B.** "Nevertheless, the skunk was in the hole."

○ **C.** "It is difficult to recall the exact sequence of action,"

○ **D.** "The skunk showed no inclination to climb it,"

COMMON CORE STATE STANDARDS

Literature 1. Quote accurately from a text when explaining what the text says explicitly and when drawing inferences from the text. **Literature 3.** Compare and contrast two or more characters, settings, or events in a story or drama, drawing on specific details in the text (e.g., how characters interact).

Next

Vocabulary

Directions: Read the questions below and choose the best answer.

4. **Part A**

The Latin prefixes "sub-" and "sus-" mean "up from under." The Latin word "pendere" means "to hang." Use these meanings to figure out the meaning of the word "suspended" in the last paragraph.

- ○ **A.** floated, as if tied to a string from a ceiling
- ○ **B.** slid down, as if on a long playground slide
- ○ **C.** swung around in a large circle, as if tied to a rope
- ○ **D.** vanished, as if through magic

Part B

Which detail from the passage also helped you figure out the meaning of the word?

- ○ **A.** Mr. Muldoon disappears.
- ○ **B.** The hat remains in the air.
- ○ **C.** Mr. Muldoon falls into the hole.
- ○ **D.** The hat falls into the hole.

COMMON CORE STATE STANDARDS

Literature 4. Determine the meaning of words and phrases as they are used in a text, including figurative language such as metaphors and similes. **Language 4.a.** Use context (e.g., cause/effect relationships and comparisons in text) as a clue to the meaning of a word or phrase. **Language 4.b.** Use common, grade-appropriate Greek and Latin affixes and roots as clues to the meaning of a word (e.g., *photograph*, *photosynthesis*).

Name _____

5. **Part A**

Based on context clues, what is the meaning of the word "hollowed" in the following sentences?

"Eddie and I went back out to the hole and stuck the ladder in it. The skunk showed no inclination to climb it, choosing instead to hide in the cavern it had hollowed out."

- ○ **A.** shouted
- ○ **B.** emptied
- ○ **C.** raised
- ○ **D.** smelled

Part B

Which context clue helped you answer Part A?

- ○ **A.** "skunk"
- ○ **B.** "climb"
- ○ **C.** "instead"
- ○ **D.** "cavern"

COMMON CORE STATE STANDARDS

Literature 4. Determine the meaning of words and phrases as they are used in a text, including figurative language such as metaphors and similes. **Language 4.a.** Use context (e.g., cause/effect relationships and comparisons in text) as a clue to the meaning of a word or phrase.

Next

6. **Part A**

What does the word "growled" mean in the following sentence?

"'I thought I told you not to build anything,' he growled."

- ○ **A.** He shouted loudly, as if to warn them.
- ○ **B.** He spoke in a manner that sounded like a barking dog.
- ○ **C.** He howled in a high-pitched scream of victory.
- ○ **D.** He grumbled the message, using a low voice.

Part B

Which detail helped you figure out the meaning of the word "growled"?

- ○ **A.** Eddie's father doesn't want skunks in his shop.
- ○ **B.** Eddie forgot that his father didn't want him in his shop.
- ○ **C.** Eddie's father is a little angry that the friends disobeyed him.
- ○ **D.** Eddie has brilliant ideas that sometimes do not work out well.

COMMON CORE STATE STANDARDS

Literature 4. Determine the meaning of words and phrases as they are used in a text, including figurative language such as metaphors and similes. **Language 4.a.** Use context (e.g., cause/effect relationships and comparisons in text) as a clue to the meaning of a word or phrase.

Next

Writing – Constructed Response

Based on the information in the passage from the selection *The Skunk Ladder,* write a paragraph about the intentions of the two friends. Apparently they decided to keep the hole and the skunk a secret from Eddie's father. Do you think this is a good idea or a bad idea? Why?

State your opinion and support it with reasons. Use your own ideas as well as details from the text. Conclude with a sentence that restates your opinion.

_____

_____

_____

_____

_____

_____

_____

_____

_____

_____

_____

_____

To the Teacher: Use the Writing Rubric on page T17 to assess students' writing.

COMMON CORE STATE STANDARDS

Literature 1. Quote accurately from a text when explaining what the text says explicitly and when drawing inferences from the text. **Writing 1.** Write opinion pieces on topics or texts, supporting a point of view with reasons and information. **Writing 1.a.** Introduce a topic or text clearly, state an opinion, and create an organizational structure in which ideas are logically grouped to support the writer's purpose. **Writing 1.b.** Provide logically ordered reasons that are supported by facts and details. **Writing 1.d.** Provide a concluding statement or section related to the opinion presented. **Writing 4.** Produce clear and coherent writing in which the development and organization are appropriate to task, purpose, and audience. **Writing 9.** Draw evidence from literary or informational texts to support analysis, reflection, and research. **Language 1.** Demonstrate command of the conventions of standard English grammar and usage when writing or speaking. **Language 2.** Demonstrate command of the conventions of standard English capitalization, punctuation, and spelling when writing.

Next

Writing – Extended Response

You have read two texts about the adventures of a young person and a good friend.

- *The Skunk Ladder*
- "Books and Adventure"

Think about why people enjoy reading stories about friends. What is the appeal of these stories? What types of lessons might these stories offer to the readers? Write an essay in which you address these questions. Introduce the topic and then develop it with facts, details, and examples from the selections. Tell general observations and group related information logically. Provide a concluding statement that sums up your main points. Remember to follow the conventions of standard English grammar, capitalization, punctuation, and spelling.

To the Teacher: Tell students they may use the space on this page to plan their writing. Then have them write their response on the following pages. Use the Writing Rubric on page T18 to assess students' writing.

COMMON CORE STATE STANDARDS

Literature 1. Quote accurately from a text when explaining what the text says explicitly and when drawing inferences from the text. **Writing 2.** Write informative/explanatory texts to examine a topic and convey ideas and information clearly. **Writing 2.a.** Introduce a topic clearly, provide a general observation and focus, and group related information logically; include formatting (e.g., headings), illustrations, and multimedia when useful to aiding comprehension. **Writing 2.b.** Develop the topic with facts, definitions, concrete details, quotations, or other information and examples related to the topic. **Writing 2.e.** Provide a concluding statement or section related to the information or explanation presented. **Writing 4.** Produce clear and coherent writing in which the development and organization are appropriate to task, purpose, and audience. **Writing 9.** Draw evidence from literary or informational texts to support analysis, reflection, and research. **Language 1.** Demonstrate command of the conventions of standard English grammar and usage when writing or speaking. **Language 2.** Demonstrate command of the conventions of standard English capitalization, punctuation, and spelling when writing.

Next

Name _____

_____

_____

_____

_____

_____

_____

_____

_____

_____

_____

_____

_____

_____

_____

_____

_____

_____

_____

Next

_____

_____

_____

_____

_____

_____

_____

_____

_____

_____

_____

_____

_____

_____

_____

_____

_____

_____

_____

_____

Name _____

Directions: Read the following passage. Use information from the passage to answer the questions.

The Unsinkable Wreck of the R.M.S. *Titanic*

by Robert D. Ballard and Rick Archbold

Inside the cramped submarine, all I could hear was the steady pinging of the sonar and the regular breathing of the pilot and engineer. I crouched on my knees, my eyes glued to the tiny viewport. The pings speeded up—that meant the wreck was close—and I strained to see beyond the small cone of light that pierced the endless underwater night.

"Come right!" I was so excited I was almost shouting, even though the two others with me inside *Alvin* were so close I could touch them. "Bingo!"

Like a ghost from the ancient past, the bow of the Royal Mail Steamer *Titanic,* the greatest shipwreck of all time, materialized out my viewport. After years of questing, I had arrived at the ship's last resting place.

Effortlessly we rose up the side of the famous bow, now weeping great tears of rust, past the huge anchor and up over the rail. We were the first in more than seventy years to "walk" on the *Titanic*'s deck! The giant windlasses used for raising and lowering the anchor still trailed their massive links of chain, as if ready to lower away. I felt as though I had walked into a dream.

In 1912, the *Titanic* had set sail on her maiden voyage, the largest, most luxurious ship the world had ever seen. On board were many of the rich and famous of the day. Then, on the fifth night out—tragedy. An iceberg, seen too late. Too few lifeboats. Pandemonium, and over 1,500 dead out of the more than 2,200 people on board.

Now the sub sailed out over the well deck, following the angle of the fallen foremast up toward the liner's bridge. We paused at the crow's nest. On the fateful night, lookout Frederick Fleet had been on duty here. It was he who warned the bridge: "Iceberg right ahead." Fleet was one of the lucky ones. He made it into a lifeboat and to safety.

Next

The pilot set *Alvin* gently down on the bridge, not far from the telemotor control—all that remained of the steering mechanism of the ship. It was here that First Officer William Murdoch, desperate to avoid the mountain of ice that lay in the *Titanic*'s path, shouted to the helmsman, "Hard a-starboard!" Then Murdoch watched in excruciating agony as the huge ship slowly began to turn—but it was too late and the iceberg fatally grazed the liner's side. I thought of Captain E. J. Smith rushing from his cabin to be told the terrible news. Thirty minutes later, after learning how quickly water was pouring into the ship, he knew that the "unsinkable" *Titanic* was doomed.

We lifted off from the bridge and headed toward the stern. Over a doorway we could make out the brass plate with the words: 1st Class Entrance. In my mind's eye I could see the deck surging with passengers as the crew tried to keep order during the loading of the lifeboats. The broken arm of a lifeboat davit hung over the side. From this spot port-side lifeboat No. 2 was launched—barely half full. Among the twenty-five people in a boat designed to carry more than forty were Minnie Coutts and her two boys, Willie and Neville. They were among the relatively few third-class passengers to survive the sinking.

As our tiny submarine continued toward the stern, we peered through the windows of first-class staterooms. The glass dome over the first-class grand staircase was long gone, providing a perfect opening for exploring the interior of the ship. But that would have to wait for a later visit, when we would bring along our robotic "swimming eyeball," *Jason Junior*. As we continued back, I wondered what we would find. . . .

Text-Based Comprehension

Directions: Read the questions below and choose the best answer.

1. **Part A**

   Which type of graphic would be most helpful to understand what the author saw?

   ○ **A.** a map showing the journey of the *Alvin*
   ○ **B.** a photograph of the *Jason Junior*
   ○ **C.** a diagram of the *Alvin*
   ○ **D.** a diagram of the *Titanic*

   Part B

   Which detail from the passage best supports your answer to Part A?

   ○ **A.** "and I strained to see beyond the small cone of light"
   ○ **B.** "we peered through the windows of first-class staterooms."
   ○ **C.** "After years of questing, I had arrived at the ship's last resting place."
   ○ **D.** "we would bring along our robotic 'swimming eyeball,' *Jason Junior*."

COMMON CORE STATE STANDARDS

Informational Text 1. Quote accurately from a text when explaining what the text says explicitly and when drawing inferences from the text. **Informational Text 7.** Draw on information from multiple print or digital sources, demonstrating the ability to locate an answer to a question quickly or to solve a problem efficiently.

Next

2. **Part A**

What is the unstated main idea of the next-to-last paragraph?

○ **A.** The *Alvin* had to travel slowly to see details through the water.

○ **B.** Most of the *Titanic's* lifeboats sank.

○ **C.** When the *Titanic* sank, there was much commotion on the deck.

○ **D.** The rich and famous passengers on the ship did not mingle with the third-class passengers.

Part B

Which detail from the paragraph does **not** support this main idea?

○ **A.** "We lifted off from the bridge and headed toward the stern."

○ **B.** "In my mind's eye I could see the deck surging with passengers"

○ **C.** "From this spot port-side lifeboat No. 2 was launched—barely half full."

○ **D.** "Pandemonium, and over 1,500 dead"

COMMON CORE STATE STANDARDS

Informational Text 1. Quote accurately from a text when explaining what the text says explicitly and when drawing inferences from the text. **Informational Text 2.** Determine two or more main ideas of a text and explain how they are supported by key details; summarize the text.

Next

3. **Part A**

What is one of the author's purposes for telling stories about the *Titanic* before it sank?

○ **A.** to give facts about the discovery of the shipwreck

○ **B.** to illustrate how the *Titanic* was poorly constructed

○ **C.** to make the reader wonder what will happen next

○ **D.** to educate the reader about the history of the *Titanic*

Part B

Which detail from the text best supports your answer to Part A?

○ **A.** "On the fateful night, lookout Frederick Fleet had been on duty here."

○ **B.** "I felt as though I had walked into a dream."

○ **C.** "The pings speeded up—that meant the wreck was close"

○ **D.** "following the angle of the fallen foremast up toward the liner's bridge."

COMMON CORE STATE STANDARDS

Informational Text 1. Quote accurately from a text when explaining what the text says explicitly and when drawing inferences from the text.

Next

Vocabulary

Directions: Read the questions below and choose the best answer.

4. **Part A**

   Based on context clues, what is the best definition of the word "helmsman"
   in the following sentence?

   "It was here that First Officer William Murdoch, desperate to avoid the
   mountain of ice that lay in the *Titanic*'s path, shouted to the helmsman,
   'Hard a-starboard!'"

   ○ **A.** someone who builds a ship
   ○ **B.** someone who captains a ship
   ○ **C.** someone who steers a ship
   ○ **D.** someone who takes care of passengers on a ship

   Part B

   Which context clue from the passage helped you answer Part A?

   ○ **A.** "down on the bridge,"
   ○ **B.** "ship slowly began to turn"
   ○ **C.** "grazed the liner's side"
   ○ **D.** "Captain E. J. Smith"

COMMON CORE STATE STANDARDS

Informational Text 4. Determine the meaning of general academic and domain-specific words and
phrases in a text relevant to a *grade 5 topic or subject area*. **Language 4.** Determine or clarify the meaning
of unknown and multiple-meaning words and phrases based on *grade 5 reading and content*, choosing
flexibly from a range of strategies. **Language 4.a.** Use context (e.g., cause/effect relationships and
comparisons in text) as a clue to the meaning of a word or phrase.

Next

5. **Part A**

Which meaning of the word "arm" is used in the following sentence?

"The broken arm of a lifeboat davit hung over the side."

○ **A.** a body part of a person

○ **B.** a support piece of a chair or couch

○ **C.** a thin, extended part of a machine

○ **D.** a specific part of an organization

Part B

Which detail from the sentence is the best clue to the meaning of the word?

○ **A.** "lifeboat davit"

○ **B.** "over"

○ **C.** "hung"

○ **D.** "the side"

COMMON CORE STATE STANDARDS

Informational Text 4. Determine the meaning of general academic and domain-specific words and phrases in a text relevant to a *grade 5 topic or subject area.* **Language 4.** Determine or clarify the meaning of unknown and multiple-meaning words and phrases based on *grade 5 reading and content,* choosing flexibly from a range of strategies. **Language 4.a.** Use context (e.g., cause/effect relationships and comparisons in text) as a clue to the meaning of a word or phrase.

Next

6. **Part A**

   This detail from the selection contains a metaphor: "Effortlessly we rose up the side of the famous bow, now weeping great tears of rust." What does the metaphor mean?

   ○ **A.** The ship was ripped open, and the rip was rusty.

   ○ **B.** This area of the ship had streaks of rust on it.

   ○ **C.** The explorers started crying and could not stop.

   ○ **D.** The ship had actual tears leaking out of it.

   Part B

   Which detail about the passage helped you answer Part A?

   ○ **A.** The *Titanic* was a giant ship.

   ○ **B.** The *Titanic* hit an iceberg, causing water to enter.

   ○ **C.** The *Titanic* had been underwater for years.

   ○ **D.** The *Titanic* was found using sonar.

COMMON CORE STATE STANDARDS

Informational Text 4. Determine the meaning of general academic and domain-specific words and phrases in a text relevant to a *grade 5 topic or subject area.* **Language 4.** Determine or clarify the meaning of unknown and multiple-meaning words and phrases based on *grade 5 reading and content,* choosing flexibly from a range of strategies. **Language 4.a.** Use context (e.g., cause/effect relationships and comparisons in text) as a clue to the meaning of a word or phrase. **Language 5.a.** Interpret figurative language, including similes and metaphors, in context.

Next

Writing – Constructed Response

Based on the information in the passage from the selection *The Unsinkable Wreck of the R.M.S.* Titanic, write a three-question interview about seeing the wreck of the *Titanic* for the first time. Imagine you were the pilot or engineer aboard the *Alvin*.

Use details from the text to describe the setting. Organize the interview questions so the events are in a clear sequence. Use dialogue, description, and sensory details to convey what the experience was like.

_____

_____

_____

_____

_____

_____

_____

_____

_____

_____

To the Teacher: Use the Writing Rubric on page T17 to assess students' writing.

COMMON CORE STATE STANDARDS

Informational Text 1. Quote accurately from a text when explaining what the text says explicitly and when drawing inferences from the text. **Writing 3.** Write narratives to develop real or imagined experiences or events using effective technique, descriptive details, and clear event sequences. **Writing 3.a.** Orient the reader by establishing a situation and introducing a narrator and/or characters; organize an event sequence that unfolds naturally. **Writing 3.b.** Use narrative techniques, such as dialogue, description, and pacing, to develop experiences and events or show the responses of characters to situations. **Writing 3.d.** Use concrete words and phrases and sensory details to convey experiences and events precisely. **Writing 4.** Produce clear and coherent writing in which the development and organization are appropriate to task, purpose, and audience. **Writing 9.** Draw evidence from literary or informational texts to support analysis, reflection, and research. **Language 1.** Demonstrate command of the conventions of standard English grammar and usage when writing or speaking. **Language 2.** Demonstrate command of the conventions of standard English capitalization, punctuation, and spelling when writing.

Next

Writing – Extended Response

You have read two texts about people attempting to solve a problem in a unique way.

- *The Unsinkable Wreck of the R.M.S.* Titanic
- *The Skunk Ladder*

Despite vast differences in their characters and settings, these two stories have important similarities in their plots and in the lessons they teach. Write an essay in which you compare the stories' plots and the problem each story attempts to solve. Introduce the topic and then develop it with facts, details, and examples from the selections. Provide a concluding statement that sums up your main points. Remember to follow the conventions of standard English grammar, capitalization, punctuation, and spelling.

To the Teacher: Tell students they may use the space on this page to plan their writing. Then have them write their response on the following pages. Use the Writing Rubric on page T18 to assess students' writing.

COMMON CORE STATE STANDARDS

Informational Text 1. Quote accurately from a text when explaining what the text says explicitly and when drawing inferences from the text. **Writing 2.** Write informative/explanatory texts to examine a topic and convey ideas and information clearly. **Writing 2.a.** Introduce a topic clearly, provide a general observation and focus, and group related information logically; include formatting (e.g., headings), illustrations, and multimedia when useful to aiding comprehension. **Writing 2.b.** Develop the topic with facts, definitions, concrete details, quotations, or other information and examples related to the topic. **Writing 2.e.** Provide a concluding statement or section related to the information or explanation presented. **Language 1.** Demonstrate command of the conventions of standard English grammar and usage when writing or speaking. **Language 2.** Demonstrate command of the conventions of standard English capitalization, punctuation, and spelling when writing.

Next

Name _____

_____

_____

_____

_____

_____

_____

_____

_____

_____

_____

_____

_____

_____

_____

_____

_____

_____

_____

_____

_____

_____

_____

_____

_____

_____

_____

_____

_____

_____

_____

_____

_____

_____

_____

_____

_____

_____

_____

Name _____

Directions: Read the following passage. Use information from the passage to answer the questions.

Talk with an Astronaut

Ellen Ochoa is the first Hispanic American woman to fly in space. She is also an inventor of optical and robotic devices. She was interviewed by fifth-grade students.

Q. Why did you want to go into space?

A. I can't imagine not wanting to go into space. But I never considered being an astronaut as an option because when I was growing up there were no female astronauts. It wasn't until the first six female astronauts were selected in 1978 that women could even think of it as a possible career path.

Q. What is it like to operate a robot arm in space?

A. I have worked the robot arm on all three of my space missions, and I really love it. It's challenging to do, but lots of fun. On my last mission to the space station I worked with the help of cameras and monitors because we were docked in a way that prevented me from seeing the robot arm. This made things more difficult, but then again, everything I've done on actual missions in space has always been easier than when I first tried it during training.

Q. What is NASA training like?

A. Everything is always harder to do in training. In training, we prepare for anything that could happen on a space mission—anything that could go wrong. In training, things keep breaking, problems have to be solved. Nothing has ever gone wrong on any of my missions, and our training helps us make sure that nothing will. Each mission has its own specific purpose. For my last mission, we trained for nine months before the actual flight. I started my formal NASA training in 1990. During that period I spent about half the time in training; the other half I spent performing other duties. I was in training for three years before my first mission, which isn't that long of a wait. Some astronauts have waited 10, even 16 years before they finally go into space!

Next

Q. What is it like to float in zero gravity?

A. Weightlessness is the fun part of the mission. There is really nothing to compare it to on Earth. I guess the closest thing would be swimming or scuba diving. It's a similar freedom of movement. What is odd is that weightlessness seems more natural. You don't have the same kinds of sensations in space as you do in the water.

Q. How do you sleep on the space shuttle? Does everyone sleep at the same time, or do you take turns? Do you have weird dreams because you're sleeping in space?

A. On my first two missions we slept in two shifts. We had sleeping compartments that looked like coffins. On my last mission we slept in a single shift. Instead of the sleeping compartments, we slept in what can best be described as a sleeping bag with hooks. You would find a place to hook on to and float in. As for my dreaming, it isn't that different in space. I tend to dream a lot, whether I'm in space or at home on Earth. I have floating dreams on Earth and non-floating dreams on a mission in space. . . .

Q. I love math and I want to become an astronaut. What can I start to do to prepare myself?

A. It is good that you love math, because in order to be an astronaut, a college degree in math or a technical science is very important to have. Being an astronaut isn't just the science, though. An astronaut must be both a team player and a leader as well. You should get involved in activities where you work closely with other people—because working closely with other people is an essential part of being an astronaut!

Next

Text-Based Comprehension

Directions: Read the questions below and choose the best answer.

1. **Part A**

   What is one of the author's purposes for the question and answer pair about NASA training?

   ○ **A.** to tell specific examples about NASA training

   ○ **B.** to tell how thorough NASA training is

   ○ **C.** to tell when astronauts begin their NASA training

   ○ **D.** to tell when astronauts go in space after NASA training

   Part B

   Which detail from the text does **not** support your answer to Part A?

   ○ **A.** "we prepare for anything that could happen on a space mission"

   ○ **B.** "Everything is always harder to do in training."

   ○ **C.** "In training, . . . problems have to be solved."

   ○ **D.** "Each mission has its own specific purpose."

COMMON CORE STATE STANDARDS

Informational Text 1. Quote accurately from a text when explaining what the text says explicitly and when drawing inferences from the text. **Informational Text 3.** Explain the relationships or interactions between two or more individuals, events, ideas, or concepts in a historical, scientific, or technical text based on specific information in the text. **Informational Text 8.** Explain how an author uses reasons and evidence to support particular points in a text, identifying which reasons and evidence support which point(s).

Next

2. **Part A**

Which is an effect caused by zero gravity and weightlessness?

○ **A.** An astronaut drifts through the air.

○ **B.** It makes an astronaut shorter.

○ **C.** An astronaut can drown.

○ **D.** It reminds an astronaut of Earth.

Part B

Which detail from the passage supports your answer to Part A?

○ **A.** "I guess the closest thing would be swimming or scuba diving."

○ **B.** "What is it like to float in zero gravity?"

○ **C.** "There is really nothing to compare it to on Earth."

○ **D.** "You don't have the same kinds of sensations in space"

COMMON CORE STATE STANDARDS

Informational Text 1. Quote accurately from a text when explaining what the text says explicitly and when drawing inferences from the text. **Informational Text 3.** Explain the relationships or interactions between two or more individuals, events, ideas, or concepts in a historical, scientific, or technical text based on specific information in the text.

Next

Name _____

3. **Part A**

Which detail from the passage is an opinion?

○ **A.** "Each mission has its own specific purpose."

○ **B.** "How do you sleep on the space shuttle?"

○ **C.** "On my last mission we slept in a single shift."

○ **D.** "Weightlessness is the fun part of the mission."

Part B

What helped you identify the detail as an opinion?

○ **A.** a question mark

○ **B.** the phrase "On my last"

○ **C.** the word "fun"

○ **D.** the word "purpose"

COMMON CORE STATE STANDARDS

Informational Text 1. Quote accurately from a text when explaining what the text says explicitly and when drawing inferences from the text. **Informational Text 8.** Explain how an author uses reasons and evidence to support particular points in a text, identifying which reasons and evidence support which point(s).

Next

Vocabulary

Directions: Read the questions below and choose the best answer.

4. **Part A**

   Which meaning of the word "degree" is used in the last question and answer pair?

   ○ **A.** an award that is given when school is completed
   ○ **B.** a unit of measurement for a circle
   ○ **C.** a unit of measurement for temperature
   ○ **D.** how intense something is

   Part B

   Which word from the sentence is the best clue to the meaning of "degree"?

   ○ **A.** "astronaut"
   ○ **B.** "good"
   ○ **C.** "important"
   ○ **D.** "college"

COMMON CORE STATE STANDARDS

Informational Text 4. Determine the meaning of general academic and domain-specific words and phrases in a text relevant to a *grade 5 topic or subject area.* **Language 4.** Determine or clarify the meaning of unknown and multiple-meaning words and phrases based on *grade 5 reading and content,* choosing flexibly from a range of strategies. **Language 4.a.** Use context (e.g., cause/effect relationships and comparisons in text) as a clue to the meaning of a word or phrase. **Language 5.c.** Use the relationship between particular words (e.g., synonyms, antonyms, homographs) to better understand each of the words.

Next

Name _____

5. **Part A**

Based on context clues in the passage, what is the best definition of the word "option" in the first question and answer pair?

○ **A.** pilot

○ **B.** guess

○ **C.** choice

○ **D.** value

Part B

Which context clue helped you answer Part A?

○ **A.** "a possible career path."

○ **B.** "go into space."

○ **C.** "the first six female"

○ **D.** "I never considered"

COMMON CORE STATE STANDARDS

Informational Text 4. Determine the meaning of general academic and domain-specific words and phrases in a text relevant to a *grade 5 topic or subject area.* **Language 4.** Determine or clarify the meaning of unknown and multiple-meaning words and phrases based on *grade 5 reading and content,* choosing flexibly from a range of strategies. **Language 4.a.** Use context (e.g., cause/effect relationships and comparisons in text) as a clue to the meaning of a word or phrase.

Next

6. **Part A**

In the question and answer pair about the robot arm, which word is the closest antonym for the word "easier"?

○ A. "prevented"
○ B. "challenging"
○ C. "tried"
○ D. "seeing"

Part B

Which word from the selection is also an antonym for "easier"?

○ A. "training"
○ B. "involved"
○ C. "difficult"
○ D. "essential"

COMMON CORE STATE STANDARDS

Informational Text 4. Determine the meaning of general academic and domain-specific words and phrases in a text relevant to a *grade 5 topic or subject area.* **Language 4.** Determine or clarify the meaning of unknown and multiple-meaning words and phrases based on *grade 5 reading and content,* choosing flexibly from a range of strategies. **Language 5.c.** Use the relationship between particular words (e.g., synonyms, antonyms, homographs) to better understand each of the words.

Next

Name _____

Writing – Constructed Response

Based on the information in the passage from the selection *Talk with an Astronaut,* write a letter from Ellen Ochoa to a childhood friend telling about her career as an astronaut. Remember to tell about the experience from Ellen Ochoa's point of view.

Establish the situation and use description to develop events. Use sensory details to convey Ellen Ochoa's experiences precisely. Add a conclusion that tells how Ellen Ochoa feels about being an astronaut.

_____

_____

_____

_____

_____

_____

_____

_____

_____

To the Teacher: Use the Writing Rubric on page T17 to assess students' writing.

COMMON CORE STATE STANDARDS

Informational Text 1. Quote accurately from a text when explaining what the text says explicitly and when drawing inferences from the text. **Writing 3.** Write narratives to develop real or imagined experiences or events using effective technique, descriptive details, and clear event sequences. **Writing 3.a.** Orient the reader by establishing a situation and introducing a narrator and/or characters; organize an event sequence that unfolds naturally. **Writing 3.b.** Use narrative techniques, such as dialogue, description, and pacing, to develop experiences and events or show the responses of characters to situations. **Writing 3.d.** Use concrete words and phrases and sensory details to convey experiences and events precisely. **Writing 3.e.** Provide a conclusion that follows from the narrated experiences or events.

Next

Writing – Extended Response

You have read two texts about people who work at the job of their dreams.

- *Talk with an Astronaut*
- *The Unsinkable Wreck of the R.M.S.* Titanic

When you really enjoy your job, it will never feel like work.

Write an opinion essay in which you agree or disagree with this idea. Begin by stating your opinion. Then offer two or more reasons, each supported by details, facts, and examples from the texts. Group your ideas logically. Provide a concluding sentence that restates your opinion. Remember to follow the conventions of standard English grammar, capitalization, punctuation, and spelling.

To the Teacher: Tell students they may use the space on this page to plan their writing. Then have them write their response on the following pages. Use the Writing Rubric on page T18 to assess students' writing.

COMMON CORE STATE STANDARDS

Informational Text 1. Quote accurately from a text when explaining what the text says explicitly and when drawing inferences from the text. **Writing 1.** Write opinion pieces on topics or texts, supporting a point of view with reasons and information. **Writing 1.a.** Introduce a topic or text clearly, state an opinion, and create an organizational structure in which ideas are logically grouped to support the writer's purpose. **Writing 1.b.** Provide logically ordered reasons that are supported by facts and details. **Writing 1.d.** Provide a concluding statement or section related to the opinion presented. **Writing 4.** Produce clear and coherent writing in which the development and organization are appropriate to task, purpose, and audience. **Language 1.** Demonstrate command of the conventions of standard English grammar and usage when writing or speaking. **Language 2.** Demonstrate command of the conventions of standard English capitalization, punctuation, and spelling when writing.

Name _____

_____

_____

_____

_____

_____

_____

_____

_____

_____

_____

_____

_____

_____

_____

_____

_____

_____

_____

_____

_____

Next

_____

_____

_____

_____

_____

_____

_____

_____

_____

_____

_____

_____

_____

_____

_____

_____

_____

_____

_____

_____

Name _____

Directions: Read the following passage. Use information from the passage to answer the questions.

Journey to the Center of the Earth

by Jules Verne

In 1864, when this story was written, people did not know what the center of the Earth was made of. One science fiction writer, Jules Verne, imagined what it might be like. In Verne's story, Professor von Hardwigg discovers a crater in Finland that leads to the very center of the Earth and sets out with his nephew, Harry, and a guide, Hans, to explore it. They descend many miles downward. Finally, they reach a deep ocean and decide to explore it on a raft. Young Harry keeps a diary of their adventures.

Tuesday, August 20. [The story continues.]

And so, in a thunder of broken water, the battle begins. At first I think all the other creatures have come to the surface and are taking part. *There* is a whale!—*there* a lizard!—a turtle!—and other monsters for which I can find no name. I point them out to Hans. But he shakes his head.

"*Tva!*" he cries.

"*Tva?* Two? Why does he say two? There are more than two!" I cry.

"No, Hans is right," says my uncle. "One of those monsters has the snout of a porpoise, the head of a lizard, the teeth of a crocodile . . . It is the ichthyosaurus, or great fish lizard."

"And the other?"

"The other is a serpent, but it has a turtle's shell. It is the plesiosaurus, or sea crocodile."

He is right! There seem to be half a dozen monsters, or more, but the truth is there are only two!

Next

And ours are the first human eyes ever to look at these great primitive reptiles! I am amazed by the flaming red eyes of the ichthyosaurus, each bigger than a man's head. Those eyes, I know, are of enormous strength, since they have to resist the pressure of water at the very bottom of the ocean. The creature is a hundred feet long, at least, and when I see his tail rise out of the water, angrily flicked like the hugest whip you could imagine, I can guess at his width. His jaw is larger than I'd ever dreamed a jaw could be, and I remembered that naturalists have said the jaw of the ichthyosaurus must have contained at least one hundred and eighty-two teeth. They were making their calculations, of course, from the fossilized bones of creatures they imagined had been extinct for millions of years. Now I, and Hans, and the Professor, are gazing, from our tiny raft, at a living ichthyosaurus, rising from an ocean deep inside the Earth!

The other creature is the mighty plesiosaurus, a serpent with a trunk like an immensely long cylinder, and a short thick tail and fins like the banks of oars in a Roman galley. Its body is enclosed in a shell, and its neck, flexible as a swan's, rises thirty feet above the surface of the sea.

No other human being has ever seen such a combat! They raise mountains of water, and time and again the raft seems about to be upset. Time and again we imagine we are drowned. The creatures hiss at each other—and the hissing is worse than the sound of the wildest winds you can imagine, all blowing together. Then they seize each other in a terrible grip, giant wrestlers: and then, break away again. And again comes the great hissing, the furious disturbance of the water!

And in the middle of it all, how tiny we are! We crouch on the raft, expecting that any moment it will be overturned and we shall drown in that wildly disturbed sea, hundreds of miles below the surface of the Earth: far, far from the sky, trees, the blessed fresh air!

Text-Based Comprehension

Directions: Read the questions below and choose the best answer.

1. **Part A**

   What causes Harry to first think there are six or more creatures during the sea battle?

   ○ **A.** The creatures have body parts that look like many other animals.

   ○ **B.** The creatures can split in two when they fight, to better survive.

   ○ **C.** The creatures are very large, and are the size of three other creatures.

   ○ **D.** The creatures are very loud, and make the noise of three other creatures.

   Part B

   Which detail from the passage supports your answer to Part A?

   ○ **A.** "'One . . . has the snout of a porpoise, the head of a lizard, the teeth of a crocodile'"

   ○ **B.** "He is right!"

   ○ **C.** "'Two? Why does he say two?'"

   ○ **D.** "There seem to be half a dozen monsters, or more,"

COMMON CORE STATE STANDARDS

Literature 1. Quote accurately from a text when explaining what the text says explicitly and when drawing inferences from the text.

Next

2. **Part A**

    What is the main idea of the passage?

    ○ **A.** It is dangerous to be in the middle of a sea battle.

    ○ **B.** Sea creatures have a strange body makeup.

    ○ **C.** The explorers discover a strange, unknown land.

    ○ **D.** Enormous monsters are often very violent.

    Part B

    Which detail from the passage best supports that main idea?

    ○ **A.** "And so, in a thunder of broken water, the battle begins."

    ○ **B.** "They were making their calculations, of course, from the fossilized bones"

    ○ **C.** "time and again the raft seems about to be upset."

    ○ **D.** "first human eyes ever to look at these great primitive reptiles!"

COMMON CORE STATE STANDARDS

Literature 1. Quote accurately from a text when explaining what the text says explicitly and when drawing inferences from the text. **Literature 2.** Determine a theme of a story, drama, or poem from details in the text, including how characters in a story or drama respond to challenges or how the speaker in a poem reflects upon a topic; summarize the text.

Next

3. **Part A**

What can you infer about the explorers during the sea creatures' battle?

○ **A.** They were afraid they might die.

○ **B.** They were glad they could record the battle.

○ **C.** They were upset that the monsters might get hurt.

○ **D.** They were proud their raft was strong.

Part B

Which sentence from the passage supports this inference?

○ **A.** "hundreds of miles below the surface of the Earth"

○ **B.** "'No, Hans is right,' says my uncle."

○ **C.** "they seize each other in a terrible grip,"

○ **D.** "expecting that any moment it will be overturned"

COMMON CORE STATE STANDARDS

Literature 1. Quote accurately from a text when explaining what the text says explicitly and when drawing inferences from the text. **Literature 2.** Determine a theme of a story, drama, or poem from details in the text, including how characters in a story or drama respond to challenges or how the speaker in a poem reflects upon a topic; summarize the text.

Next

Vocabulary

Directions: Read the questions below and choose the best answer.

4. **Part A**

Based on context clues in the passage, choose the best definition of the word "primitive" in the sentence: "And ours are the first human eyes ever to look at these great primitive reptiles!"

○ **A.** an animal with little coloring, red eyes, and pale skin

○ **B.** an early ancestor of a current animal

○ **C.** an animal with long bristles instead of teeth

○ **D.** an animal that can fly through the air extremely fast

Part B

Which context clue from the paragraph helped you answer Part A?

○ **A.** "His jaw is larger than I'd ever dreamed a jaw could be"

○ **B.** "And again comes the great hissing,"

○ **C.** "creatures they imagined had been extinct for millions of years."

○ **D.** "The creature is a hundred feet long, at least,"

COMMON CORE STATE STANDARDS

Language 4. Determine or clarify the meaning of unknown and multiple-meaning words and phrases based on *grade 5 reading and content*, choosing flexibly from a range of strategies. **Language 4.a.** Use context (e.g., cause/effect relationships and comparisons in text) as a clue to the meaning of a word or phrase.

Next

Name _____

5. **Part A**

Which meaning of the word "break" is used in the following sentence?

"Then they seize each other in a terrible grip, giant wrestlers: and then, break away again."

○ **A.** fracture a bone

○ **B.** make a thing useless

○ **C.** escape using force

○ **D.** rest from a task

Part B

Which word from the sentence is the best clue to the meaning of "break"?

○ **A.** "giant"

○ **B.** "seize"

○ **C.** "again"

○ **D.** "they"

COMMON CORE STATE STANDARDS

Language 4. Determine or clarify the meaning of unknown and multiple-meaning words and phrases based on *grade 5 reading and content,* choosing flexibly from a range of strategies. **Language 4.a.** Use context (e.g., cause/effect relationships and comparisons in text) as a clue to the meaning of a word or phrase.

Next

6. **Part A**

The Latin word "serpere" means "to creep." Use this meaning to figure out the meaning of the word "serpent" in the following sentence.

"The other creature is the mighty plesiosaurus, a serpent with a trunk like an immensely long cylinder, and a short thick tail and fins like the banks of oars in a Roman galley."

- ○ **A.** tailless shrimp
- ○ **B.** large boat
- ○ **C.** strong fish
- ○ **D.** long snake

Part B

Which detail from the passage also helped you figure out the meaning of the word?

- ○ **A.** The plesiosaurus has a body like a long tube.
- ○ **B.** The plesiosaurus has a short thick tail and a shell.
- ○ **C.** The plesiosaurus is large and mighty.
- ○ **D.** The plesiosaurus has oars like a Roman ship.

COMMON CORE STATE STANDARDS

Language 4. Determine or clarify the meaning of unknown and multiple-meaning words and phrases based on *grade 5 reading and content,* choosing flexibly from a range of strategies. **Language 4.a.** Use context (e.g., cause/effect relationships and comparisons in text) as a clue to the meaning of a word or phrase. **Language 4.b.** Use common, grade-appropriate Greek and Latin affixes and roots as clues to the meaning of a word (e.g., *photograph, photosynthesis*).

Next

Writing – Constructed Response

Based on the information in the passage from the selection *Journey to the Center of the Earth,* write a school news article that tells about the explorers' adventure.

Introduce the topic and then develop it using details from the text. Conclude with a sentence that sums up the description.

_____

_____

_____

_____

_____

_____

_____

_____

_____

_____

_____

_____

_____

To the Teacher: Use the Writing Rubric on page T17 to assess students' writing.

COMMON CORE STATE STANDARDS

Literature 1. Quote accurately from a text when explaining what the text says explicitly and when drawing inferences from the text. **Writing 2.** Write informative/explanatory texts to examine a topic and convey ideas and information clearly. **Writing 2.a.** Introduce a topic clearly, provide a general observation and focus, and group related information logically; include formatting (e.g., headings), illustrations, and multimedia when useful to aiding comprehension. **Writing 2.e.** Provide a concluding statement or section related to the information or explanation presented. **Writing 4.** Produce clear and coherent writing in which the development and organization are appropriate to task, purpose, and audience. **Writing 9.** Draw evidence from literary or informational texts to support analysis, reflection, and research.

Next

Writing – Extended Response

You have read two texts about people who face an unexpected situation.

- *Journey to the Center of the Earth*
- *The Skunk Ladder*

Imagine that Harry of *Journey to the Center of the Earth* and the narrator of *The Skunk Ladder* are performers at a story-telling contest. Each tells one part of their story, and the other tries to outdo them with their own story. Write two or more rounds of the competition dialogue using details from both texts. Establish the situation and organize an event sequence. Use dialogue, description, and sensory details to tell how the characters responded to experiences and events. Remember to follow the conventions of standard English capitalization, punctuation, and spelling.

To the Teacher: Tell students they may use the space on this page to plan their writing. Then have them write their response on the following pages. Use the Writing Rubric on page T18 to assess students' writing.

COMMON CORE STATE STANDARDS

Literature 1. Quote accurately from a text when explaining what the text says explicitly and when drawing inferences from the text. **Writing 3.** Write narratives to develop real or imagined experiences or events using effective technique, descriptive details, and clear event sequences. **Writing 3.d.** Use concrete words and phrases and sensory details to convey experiences and events precisely. **Writing 4.** Produce clear and coherent writing in which the development and organization are appropriate to task, purpose, and audience. **Writing 9.** Draw evidence from literary or informational texts to support analysis, reflection, and research. **Language 2.** Demonstrate command of the conventions of standard English capitalization, punctuation, and spelling when writing.

Name _____

_____

_____

_____

_____

_____

_____

_____

_____

_____

_____

_____

_____

_____

_____

_____

_____

_____

Next

_____

_____

_____

_____

_____

_____

_____

_____

_____

_____

_____

_____

_____

_____

_____

_____

_____

_____

Name _____

Directions: Read the following passage. Use information from the passage to answer the questions.

Ghost Towns of the American West

by Raymond Bial

An air of mystery swirls around the ghost towns of the American West. What sad and joyous events happened within the tumbledown walls and on the wind-blown streets? Why did people settle in these lonesome places? Why did they pull up stakes and move away? What went wrong in these towns? Virtually every ghost town has untold stories of people who longed for a chance at a better life. Relics of the past, the towns now stand as evidence of high adventure, hopes of striking it rich, and the sudden loss of fortune— or life.

Although ghost towns can be found throughout the world, in the United States they are most often thought of as the mining camps, cowboy towns, and other settlements of the sprawling western frontier.

Most were once mining camps where adventurous men came to seek their fortunes. These communities boomed as miners sought gold, silver, copper, or other precious minerals but died out when all of the ore was panned from streams or blasted from rocky tunnels. In cowboy towns, cattle were driven to other towns, and then shipped to markets in the East. Many lumber camps in deep forests and farming communities on the broad prairies also enjoyed brief prosperity before they were abandoned. Along with the miners, cowboys, and farmers, merchants and bankers, as well as doctors and schoolteachers, also went west. They laid out streets and put up buildings in hopes of growth and prosperity. As one newspaper editor declared, most folks wished "to get rich if we can."

In 1848, James W. Marshall discovered gold at Sutter's Mill when he shut down the water on the millrace and glanced into the ditch. "I reached my hand down and picked it up; it made my heart thump for I felt certain it was gold," he recalled. Soon the word was out. "Gold! Gold! Gold from the American River!" shouted Sam Brannon, waving a bottle of gold dust as he strode through the San Francisco streets. Seeking pay dirt, "forty-niners" (as the prospectors came to be known) streamed into California in the first of the great American gold rushes. Yet, over time, people came to refer to the sawmill as "Sutter's Folly" as the land of John Sutter was overrun with prospectors. Everywhere, men claimed "squatter's rights," in which they settled on land without paying for it.

Towns sprang up overnight. Charles B. Gillespie, a miner who worked near Coloma, California, described the typical main streets of these towns as "alive with crowds." To him, the miners were ragged, dirty men who were otherwise good-natured. They were a mix of Americans and immigrants—Germans, French, and other Europeans, and gold seekers from China and Chile, along with British convicts from Australia. Mark Twain declared, "It was a driving, vigorous, restless population in those days . . . two hundred thousand *young* men—not simpering, dainty, kid-gloved weaklings, but stalwart, muscular, dauntless young braves, brimful of push and energy." . . .

John Steele described Washington, California, in the 1840s, just six months after it had been founded: "With a large number of vacant cabins it contained several empty buildings and quite a large hotel, closed and silent." Once ringing with the voices of cheerful people, the towns have now fallen silent. They have become little more than empty shells of their former selves. There may be a handful of old false-front buildings, weathered to a haunting gray, with open doorways and broken windows. But little else remains; few people even remember the place. Even the memories, along with the hopes and dreams of the inhabitants, have blown away, like so much dust in the wind.

Next

Name _____

Text-Based Comprehension

Directions: Read the questions below and choose the best answer.

1. **Part A**

   What caused the now–ghost towns to first be formed?

   ○ **A.** Miners needed to settle in a town.

   ○ **B.** Cowboys needed to settle in a town.

   ○ **C.** Workers in lumber camps needed to settle in a town.

   ○ **D.** All the above reasons caused the towns to first be formed.

   Part B

   Which detail from the passage does **not** support your answer to Part A?

   ○ **A.** "Seeking pay dirt, 'forty-niners' . . . streamed into California"

   ○ **B.** "Many lumber camps . . . enjoyed brief prosperity"

   ○ **C.** "ghost towns can be found throughout the world,"

   ○ **D.** "evidence of high adventure, . . . and the sudden loss of fortune"

COMMON CORE STATE STANDARDS

Informational Text 1. Quote accurately from a text when explaining what the text says explicitly and when drawing inferences from the text. **Informational Text 2.** Determine two or more main ideas of a text and explain how they are supported by key details; summarize the text. **Informational Text 3.** Explain the relationships or interactions between two or more individuals, events, ideas, or concepts in a historical, scientific, or technical text based on specific information in the text.

Next

2. **Part A**

Which of these events happened first at Sutter's Mill?

○ **A.** The town becomes a ghost town.

○ **B.** Squatters arrive, claiming land.

○ **C.** The mill is known as "Sutter's Folly."

○ **D.** Water to a mill is stopped.

Part B

Which phrase from the passage helped you sequence the events in Part A?

○ **A.** "when he shut down . . . and glanced"

○ **B.** "the first of the . . . gold rushes."

○ **C.** "the land . . . was overrun with prospectors."

○ **D.** "Yet, over time,"

COMMON CORE STATE STANDARDS

Informational Text 1. Quote accurately from a text when explaining what the text says explicitly and when drawing inferences from the text. **Informational Text 3.** Explain the relationships or interactions between two or more individuals, events, ideas, or concepts in a historical, scientific, or technical text based on specific information in the text.

Next

3. **Part A**

What is the unstated main idea of the last paragraph?

○ **A.** It is difficult to find ghost towns on a map.

○ **B.** Ghost towns are abandoned and forgotten.

○ **C.** Towns become ghost towns after many years.

○ **D.** Washington, California, disappeared when it was blown away.

Part B

Which detail from the passage does **not** support this main idea?

○ **A.** "it contained several empty buildings"

○ **B.** "Even the memories, . . . have blown away,"

○ **C.** "open doorways and broken windows."

○ **D.** "'a driving, vigorous, restless population'"

COMMON CORE STATE STANDARDS

Informational Text 1. Quote accurately from a text when explaining what the text says explicitly and when drawing inferences from the text. **Informational Text 2.** Determine two or more main ideas of a text and explain how they are supported by key details; summarize the text.

Next

Vocabulary

Directions: Read the questions below and choose the best answer.

4. **Part A**

One meaning of the Latin prefix "in-" is "into." The Latin word "habitare" means "to dwell or live." Use these meanings to best define the meaning of the word "inhabitants" in the last paragraph.

○ **A.** people who live in ghost towns

○ **B.** people who have moved away from a town

○ **C.** people who live in a particular town

○ **D.** people who want to move to a particular town

Part B

Which detail from the paragraph also helped you figure out the meaning of the word?

○ **A.** "Once ringing with the voices of cheerful people,"

○ **B.** "described Washington, California, in the 1840s,"

○ **C.** "old false-front buildings, weathered to a haunting gray,"

○ **D.** "little else remains; few people even remember the place."

COMMON CORE STATE STANDARDS

Informational Text 4. Determine the meaning of general academic and domain-specific words and phrases in a text relevant to a *grade 5 topic or subject area*. **Foundational Skills 3.a.** Use combined knowledge of all letter-sound correspondences, syllabication patterns, and morphology (e.g., roots and affixes) to read accurately unfamiliar multisyllabic words in context and out of context. **Language 4.** Determine or clarify the meaning of unknown and multiple-meaning words and phrases based on *grade 5 reading and content,* choosing flexibly from a range of strategies. **Language 4.a.** Use context (e.g., cause/ effect relationships and comparisons in text) as a clue to the meaning of a word or phrase. **Language 4.b.** Use common, grade-appropriate Greek and Latin affixes and roots as clues to the meaning of a word (e.g., *photograph, photosynthesis*).

Next

5. **Part A**

In the paragraph containing Mark Twain's quote, what is the best definition of the word "stalwart" based on context clues?

○ **A.** angry and brave
○ **B.** strong and healthy
○ **C.** quiet and calm
○ **D.** focused and purposeful

Part B

Which context clue from the passage helped you answer Part A?

○ **A.** "population"
○ **B.** "vigorous"
○ **C.** "two hundred thousand"
○ **D.** "dirty"

COMMON CORE STATE STANDARDS

Informational Text 4. Determine the meaning of general academic and domain-specific words and phrases in a text relevant to a *grade 5 topic or subject area.* **Language 4.** Determine or clarify the meaning of unknown and multiple-meaning words and phrases based on *grade 5 reading and content,* choosing flexibly from a range of strategies. **Language 4.a.** Use context (e.g., cause/effect relationships and comparisons in text) as a clue to the meaning of a word or phrase.

6. **Part A**

What is the meaning of the idiom "air of mystery" in the first paragraph?

○ **A.** a cloud of dust, seen everywhere one looks

○ **B.** a feeling of unanswered questions

○ **C.** a foul odor that is in the air

○ **D.** a feeling of being watched by people who are dead

Part B

Which detail helped you figure out the meaning of the idiom?

○ **A.** the people moved away from the towns

○ **B.** the old American West is known for wilderness

○ **C.** the many questions that are listed in the paragraph

○ **D.** the passage is about ghost towns

COMMON CORE STATE STANDARDS

Informational Text 4. Determine the meaning of general academic and domain-specific words and phrases in a text relevant to a *grade 5 topic or subject area.* **Language 4.** Determine or clarify the meaning of unknown and multiple-meaning words and phrases based on *grade 5 reading and content,* choosing flexibly from a range of strategies. **Language 4.a.** Use context (e.g., cause/effect relationships and comparisons in text) as a clue to the meaning of a word or phrase. **Language 5.b.** Recognize and explain the meaning of common idioms, adages, and proverbs.

Next

Writing – Constructed Response

Based on the information in the passage from the selection *Ghost Towns of the American West,* write a paragraph that describes the typical resident of a booming town that will someday become a ghost town.

Introduce the topic and then develop it using details from the text. Conclude with a sentence that sums up your main point.

_____

_____

_____

_____

_____

_____

_____

_____

_____

_____

_____

_____

_____

_____

To the Teacher: Use the Writing Rubric on page T17 to assess students' writing.

COMMON CORE STATE STANDARDS

Informational Text 1. Quote accurately from a text when explaining what the text says explicitly and when drawing inferences from the text. **Writing 2.** Write informative/explanatory texts to examine a topic and convey ideas and information clearly. **Writing 2.a.** Introduce a topic clearly, provide a general observation and focus, and group related information logically; include formatting (e.g., headings), illustrations, and multimedia when useful to aiding comprehension. **Writing 2.b.** Develop the topic with facts, definitions, concrete details, quotations, or other information and examples related to the topic. **Writing 2.e.** Provide a concluding statement or section related to the information or explanation presented. **Writing 9.** Draw evidence from literary or informational texts to support analysis, reflection, and research.

Next

Writing – Extended Response

You have read two texts about people who take great personal risks in the hopes of gaining a great reward.

- *Ghost Towns of the American West*
- *Journey to the Center of the Earth*

Think about the people who moved to booming towns to make their fortunes and the explorers who travelled through the Earth. Do you think the risk is worth the reward in either situation? Why? Write an opinion piece in which you answer these questions. State your opinion and offer reasons supported by details from the selections and your own ideas. Provide a concluding sentence that restates your opinion. Remember to follow the conventions of standard English grammar, capitalization, punctuation, and spelling.

To the Teacher: Tell students they may use the space on this page to plan their writing. Then have them write their response on the following pages. Use the Writing Rubric on page T18 to assess students' writing.

COMMON CORE STATE STANDARDS

Informational Text 1. Quote accurately from a text when explaining what the text says explicitly and when drawing inferences from the text. **Writing 1.** Write opinion pieces on topics or texts, supporting a point of view with reasons and information. **Writing 1.a.** Introduce a topic or text clearly, state an opinion, and create an organizational structure in which ideas are logically grouped to support the writer's purpose. **Writing 1.b.** Provide logically ordered reasons that are supported by facts and details. **Writing 1.d.** Provide a concluding statement or section related to the opinion presented. **Language 1.** Demonstrate command of the conventions of standard English grammar and usage when writing or speaking. **Language 2.** Demonstrate command of the conventions of standard English capitalization, punctuation, and spelling when writing.

Next

Name _____

_____

_____

_____

_____

_____

_____

_____

_____

_____

_____

_____

_____

_____

_____

_____

_____

_____

_____

_____

Name _____

Directions: Read the following passage. Use information from the passage to answer the questions.

The Truth About Austin's Amazing Bats

by Ron Fridell

Where can you see a summer sky filled with 1.5 million bats? Austin, Texas, is the place. They fly out from under the Ann W. Richards Congress Avenue Bridge around sunset. Just a few at first, like scouts sent ahead to see if the coast is clear. Then dozens more emerge, then hundreds, then thousands. The bats keep pouring out until more than a million swirl above the bridge like a bat tornado. Finally, they zoom off in all directions, while the spectators below reverberate with wonder.

The bats attract an estimated 100,000 tourists to Austin each summer, bringing in close to $10 million to Austin's tourism industry. Every night crowds gather on or near the bridge for the event. An imposing sculpture, in the shape of a bat, called *Nightwing* stands at the foot of the bridge, welcoming visitors to the sight. Even Austin's former professional hockey team, the Ice Bats, embraced the creatures. The team's mascot was a fierce-looking cartoon bat gripping a hockey stick. Austin loves its bats so much that it holds a two-day summer Bat Festival to honor the flying mammals.

Spectators watch the nightly display from all sorts of places, high and low. Some watch from up on the Congress Avenue Bridge. Others watch from the lake below. The bridge spans Town Lake on the Colorado River, where people watch the bats from rowboats, canoes, and kayaks. There is even a riverboat that gives special bat cruises. Some people spread blankets on the lake's grassy shores to watch. Nearby downtown restaurants have tables set up on patios for viewing. When the bats come out, the guests put down their knives and forks to watch a breathtaking display of nature in the city.

But once upon a time, Austin's bats were neither loved nor admired, and were breathtaking for a different reason. To a great many Austin residents the bats were a bizarre and frightening sight. The bats were also a health hazard, they insisted. After some debate, a decision was made. The bats must be removed from the bridge or destroyed.

Next

How were Austin's bats saved? The story begins in 1980. That's when workers began reconstructing the Congress Avenue Bridge. The bridge is a landmark in the heart of downtown, just ten blocks from the Texas state capitol. The engineers in charge of the project didn't know that their work would create an ideal habitat for bats. Otherwise they would not have left so many openings on the bridge's concrete underside.

The long, narrow, dark crevices became instantly popular with migrating bats, because bats prefer to make cozy spots to roost and raise their young. Most of the bats are pregnant females. In March they fly north from Mexico to give birth and raise their young, called pups. That's why in August the bridge's bat population of 1.5 million is double what it was in March. Austin's human population is about 740,000. That means that in summer, Austin has twice as many bats as people!

Why were so many people so scared of the bats beneath the bridge? The reasons are based on fear and misinformation. Fear of the dark is one reason. Many children—and even some adults—are afraid of the dark, and bats are creatures of the night. During the day they inhabit dark spaces such as caves and tunnels. At night they come out to hunt. Bats' anatomy and appearance scares some people too, with their pointed ears and noses and sharply curved wings. And when people think of bats, they often think of vampires, mythical creatures that drink blood. Or they picture a great big bat flying blindly at them and getting all tangled in their hair, or biting them and giving them rabies.

Austin resident Mari Murphy remembers how fearful Austin residents used to be. "For years, local newspapers had carried headlines like 'Bat colonies sink teeth into city' and 'Mass fear in the air as bats invade Austin,'" she writes. "Misinformation abounded, and the bats that made Austin, Texas, their summer home were regarded as something to be eliminated, not as something wonderful to see."

Next

Text-Based Comprehension

Directions: Read the questions below and choose the best answer.

1. **Part A**

   What is the main idea of the passage?

   ○ **A.** Many bats are dangerous creatures.

   ○ **B.** Most people in Austin are afraid of bats.

   ○ **C.** Bats in Austin are now a part of the city.

   ○ **D.** The best place for bats to live is in cities.

   Part B

   Which detail from the passage supports that main idea?

   ○ **A.** "Most of the bats are pregnant females."

   ○ **B.** "Austin loves its bats so much"

   ○ **C.** "At night they come out to hunt."

   ○ **D.** "How were Austin's bats saved?"

COMMON CORE STATE STANDARDS

Informational Text 1. Quote accurately from a text when explaining what the text says explicitly and when drawing inferences from the text. **Informational Text 2.** Determine two or more main ideas of a text and explain how they are supported by key details; summarize the text.

Next

2. **Part A**

Which is **not** an effect of Austin's bats?

○ **A.** The bridge where bats live was renamed after them.

○ **B.** Austin's hockey team was named after them.

○ **C.** Austin's tourism industry has increased because of them.

○ **D.** Austin holds a festival every summer because of them.

Part B

Which detail from the passage supports your answer to Part A?

○ **A.** "holds a two-day summer Bat Festival"

○ **B.** "attract an estimated 100,000 tourists to Austin"

○ **C.** "professional hockey team, the Ice Bats,"

○ **D.** "the Ann W. Richards Congress Avenue Bridge"

COMMON CORE STATE STANDARDS

Informational Text 1. Quote accurately from a text when explaining what the text says explicitly and when drawing inferences from the text.

Next

3. **Part A**

Which detail from the third paragraph contains an opinion?

- ○ **A.** "Spectators watch the nightly display from all sorts of places, high and low."
- ○ **B.** "where people watch the bats from rowboats, canoes, and kayaks."
- ○ **C.** "Nearby downtown restaurants have tables set up on patios for viewing."
- ○ **D.** "When the bats come out, . . . watch a breathtaking display of nature in city."

Part B

Which word helped you identify it as an opinion?

- ○ **A.** "breathtaking"
- ○ **B.** "people"
- ○ **C.** "Spectators"
- ○ **D.** "viewing"

COMMON CORE STATE STANDARDS

Informational Text 1. Quote accurately from a text when explaining what the text says explicitly and when drawing inferences from the text.

Next

Vocabulary

Directions: Read the questions below and choose the best answer.

4. **Part A**

Based on context clues in the passage, what is the best definition of the word "migrating" in the following sentence?

"The long, narrow, dark crevices became instantly popular with migrating bats, because bats prefer to make cozy spots to roost and raise their young."

- ○ **A.** yipping and squawking, making a loud noise
- ○ **B.** moving back and forth from one region to another
- ○ **C.** remaining still and quiet in order to avoid predators
- ○ **D.** resting and sleeping, usually for two to four months

Part B

Which detail from the paragraph helped you answer Part A?

- ○ **A.** "became instantly popular"
- ○ **B.** "bridge's bat population . . . is double what it was"
- ○ **C.** "raise their young, called pups."
- ○ **D.** "In March they fly north from Mexico"

COMMON CORE STATE STANDARDS

Informational Text 4. Determine the meaning of general academic and domain-specific words and phrases in a text relevant to a *grade 5 topic or subject area.* **Language 4.** Determine or clarify the meaning of unknown and multiple-meaning words and phrases based on *grade 5 reading and content,* choosing flexibly from a range of strategies. **Language 4.a.** Use context (e.g., cause/effect relationships and comparisons in text) as a clue to the meaning of a word or phrase.

5. **Part A**

What is the meaning of the idiom "the coast is clear" in the first paragraph?

○ **A.** there is plenty of food

○ **B.** it is safe to go forward

○ **C.** the sky is free of fog

○ **D.** the water is calm

Part B

Which context clue best helped you figure out the meaning of the idiom?

○ **A.** "can you see a summer sky"

○ **B.** "Just a few at first,"

○ **C.** "swirl above the bridge"

○ **D.** "spectators below reverberate"

COMMON CORE STATE STANDARDS

Informational Text 4. Determine the meaning of general academic and domain-specific words and phrases in a text relevant to a *grade 5 topic or subject area*. **Language 4.** Determine or clarify the meaning of unknown and multiple-meaning words and phrases based on *grade 5 reading and content,* choosing flexibly from a range of strategies. **Language 5.b.** Recognize and explain the meaning of common idioms, adages, and proverbs.

Next

6. **Part A**

The Latin word "crepare" means "to crack." Use this meaning to figure out the meaning of the word "crevices" in the following sentence.

"The long, narrow, dark crevices became instantly popular with migrating bats, because bats prefer to make cozy spots to roost and raise their young."

○ **A.** openings caused by a split

○ **B.** boats or ships on the water

○ **C.** damaged bridges in need of repair

○ **D.** damaged bat eggs in danger of spoiling

Part B

Which word from the paragraph also helped you figure out the meaning of "crevices"?

○ **A.** "spots"

○ **B.** "roost"

○ **C.** "narrow"

○ **D.** "pregnant"

COMMON CORE STATE STANDARDS

Informational Text 4. Determine the meaning of general academic and domain-specific words and phrases in a text relevant to a *grade 5 topic or subject area.* **Language 4.b.** Use common, grade-appropriate Greek and Latin affixes and roots as clues to the meaning of a word (e.g., *photograph, photosynthesis*).

Next

Name _____

Writing – Constructed Response

Based on the information in the passage from the selection *The Truth About Austin's Amazing Bats,* write a paragraph that could be used on a Web page that tells tourists about the bats in Austin.

Introduce the topic and then develop it using facts and details from the text. Group related information in a logical way. Conclude with a sentence that sums up the description.

_____

_____

_____

_____

_____

_____

_____

_____

_____

_____

_____

To the Teacher: Use the Writing Rubric on page T17 to assess students' writing.

COMMON CORE STATE STANDARDS

Informational Text 1. Quote accurately from a text when explaining what the text says explicitly and when drawing inferences from the text. **Writing 2.** Write informative/explanatory texts to examine a topic and convey ideas and information clearly. **Writing 2.a.** Introduce a topic clearly, provide a general observation and focus, and group related information logically; include formatting (e.g., headings), illustrations, and multimedia when useful to aiding comprehension. **Writing 2.b.** Develop the topic with facts, definitions, concrete details, quotations, or other information and examples related to the topic. **Writing 2.e.** Provide a concluding statement or section related to the information or explanation presented. **Writing 4.** Produce clear and coherent writing in which the development and organization are appropriate to task, purpose, and audience. **Writing 9.** Draw evidence from literary or informational texts to support analysis, reflection, and research. **Language 1.** Demonstrate command of the conventions of standard English grammar and usage when writing or speaking. **Language 2.** Demonstrate command of the conventions of standard English capitalization, punctuation, and spelling when writing.

Next

Writing – Extended Response

You have read two texts about the bats in Austin, Texas.

- *The Truth About Austin's Amazing Bats*
- "The Animals in My Life"

Imagine that the narrator in "The Animals in My Life" meets a tourist in Austin who has just seen the bats for the first time. Write a dialogue between the narrator and the tourist. Establish the situation and introduce the characters. Use dialogue, descriptions, and sensory details from the texts to show how they responded to experiences and events. Remember to follow the conventions of standard English grammar, capitalization, punctuation, and spelling.

To the Teacher: Tell students they may use the space on this page to plan their writing. Then have them write their response on the following pages. Use the Writing Rubric on page T18 to assess students' writing.

COMMON CORE STATE STANDARDS

Informational Text 1. Quote accurately from a text when explaining what the text says explicitly and when drawing inferences from the text. **Writing 3.** Write narratives to develop real or imagined experiences or events using effective technique, descriptive details, and clear event sequences. **Writing 3.a.** Orient the reader by establishing a situation and introducing a narrator and/or characters; organize an event sequence that unfolds naturally. **Writing 3.b.** Use narrative techniques, such as dialogue, description, and pacing, to develop experiences and events or show the responses of characters to situations. **Writing 3.d.** Use concrete words and phrases and sensory details to convey experiences and events precisely. **Writing 4.** Produce clear and coherent writing in which the development and organization are appropriate to task, purpose, and audience. **Writing 9.** Draw evidence from literary or informational texts to support analysis, reflection, and research. **Language 1.** Demonstrate command of the conventions of standard English grammar and usage when writing or speaking. **Language 2.** Demonstrate command of the conventions of standard English capitalization, punctuation, and spelling when writing.

Next

Name _____

_____

_____

_____

_____

_____

_____

_____

_____

_____

_____

_____

_____

_____

_____

_____

_____

_____

_____

_____

_____

Next

_____

_____

_____

_____

_____

_____

_____

_____

_____

_____

_____

_____

_____

_____

_____

_____

_____

_____

Directions: Read the following passage. Use information from the passage to answer the questions.

The Mystery of Saint Matthew Island

by Susan E. Quinlan

With the time of death narrowed down to late winter 1963–1964, Klein searched for clues about the cause of death. No predators lived on the island, and people rarely visit it. So neither of these potential killers were suspects in the case.

Klein ruled out diseases and parasites because he had found almost no signs of disease or parasites on his earlier visits to Saint Matthew. And it was not possible that an infected animal from somewhere else had brought in any disease or parasite. Saint Matthew Island is too remote.

Klein found skeletons from animals of all ages. Therefore old age was not the cause of the die-off either. That left weather and starvation as possible causes.

Weather seemed likely to be involved. The 1963–64 winter included some of the deepest snows and the coldest temperatures ever recorded in the Bering Sea area. But Klein thought a severe winter alone should not have caused such a massive die-off. Reindeer are arctic animals. As long as they have enough food, most healthy reindeer should be able to survive, even in a severe winter.

Thus Klein suspected that the Saint Matthew Island reindeer had been unhealthy or had run out of food during the winter of 1963–64. With this thought in mind, Klein looked for evidence of starvation in the skeletons. An important clue lay hidden inside the bones. A well-fed animal has fat in its bone marrow. This fatty marrow remains in the bones for five years or more after an animal dies. Knowing this, Klein cracked open the leg bones of the skeletons to examine the marrow. Bone after bone, skeleton after skeleton, the marrow was completely gone. None of the animals had fat in their bone marrow when they died. This was clear evidence that the herd had starved to death.

When Klein visited the island three years earlier, he had noticed that some important winter food plants of the reindeer looked overgrazed. When he looked around this time, he noticed more severe damage. Many of the small plants looked as if they had been clipped back. And lichens, mosslike organisms that once carpeted the island, were now absent from many areas. Klein observed that the most serious damage was on hilltops and ridges, where winds keep the ground snow-free in winter. Such places would have been used heavily by reindeer during winter.

The damaged plant life led Klein to suspect that the reindeer had run out of nutritious food. Knowing that a lack of healthy food would show up in the weights of the reindeer, Klein reviewed the records from his earlier visits to Saint Matthew. The animals he had examined in 1957 weighed 199 to 404 pounds—more than most reindeer elsewhere. Clearly, the animals had plenty of food then. In contrast, the reindeer Klein had weighed in 1963 averaged 50 to 120 pounds less in weight. These lower weights showed that when the herd had numbered six thousand animals, many of the reindeer were not getting enough to eat. Klein next weighed a few of the live reindeer that remained on the island. These animals still weighed less than normal. They were not getting enough good food. That clinched the case. Klein was now certain what had happened.

Without predators or disease to limit its numbers, the small reindeer herd had grown quickly. Many young were born, and all the animals had plenty to eat. But after a few years, there were too many animals. The reindeer ate and trampled the tundra plants and lichens faster than these could grow. Crowded onto the windswept ridges in winter, the large herd destroyed the lush lichen carpet. When the most nutritious plants and lichens became scarce, the reindeer began to lose weight. In poor condition, and with little food to sustain them, disaster was inevitable. The harsh winter of 1963–64 spelled the end for the once healthy herd. The Saint Matthew Island reindeer had literally eaten themselves out of house and home. By their numbers alone, they had destroyed their island home and their future.

Next

Text-Based Comprehension

Directions: Read the questions below and choose the best answer.

1. **Part A**

   What is the unstated main idea of the last paragraph?

   ○ **A.** Predators will reduce the population of a herd.

   ○ **B.** Poor nutrition can cause weight loss.

   ○ **C.** Reindeer are dangerous to lichens.

   ○ **D.** Overpopulation can lead to a terrible end.

   Part B

   Which detail from the paragraph best supports this main idea?

   ○ **A.** "By their numbers alone, they had destroyed . . . their future."

   ○ **B.** "Without predators or disease . . . , the small reindeer herd had grown"

   ○ **C.** "The harsh winter of 1963–64 spelled the end for the . . . herd."

   ○ **D.** "Many young were born, and all the animals had plenty to eat."

COMMON CORE STATE STANDARDS

Informational Text 1. Quote accurately from a text when explaining what the text says explicitly and when drawing inferences from the text. **Informational Text 2.** Determine two or more main ideas of a text and explain how they are supported by key details; summarize the text.

Next

2. **Part A**

According to the passage, which is a correct sequence of events?

○ **A.** Klein rules out predators as a cause; Klein determines the time of death; Klein weighs the remaining live reindeer

○ **B.** Klein determines the time of death; Klein rules out diseases as a cause; Klein examines the skeletons' bone marrow

○ **C.** Klein rules out diseases as a cause; Klein reexamines the island's plants; Klein determines the time of death

○ **D.** Klein weighs the remaining live reindeer; Klein reexamines the island's plants; Klein examines the skeletons' bone marrow

Part B

Which detail from the passage helped you choose the sequence in Part A?

○ **A.** discussion of the winter of 1963–64

○ **B.** discussion of the island's location and weather

○ **C.** the title of the passage

○ **D.** the order of the paragraphs and sentences

COMMON CORE STATE STANDARDS

Informational Text 1. Quote accurately from a text when explaining what the text says explicitly and when drawing inferences from the text. **Informational Text 3.** Explain the relationships or interactions between two or more individuals, events, ideas, or concepts in a historical, scientific, or technical text based on specific information in the text.

Next

3. **Part A**

Which is the best description of the overall structure of the passage?

○ **A.** a "Cause and Effect" text, presenting an event that happened and then telling what caused it

○ **B.** a "Compare and Contrast" text, presenting similarities and differences to describe a topic

○ **C.** a "How-To" text, presenting steps as a group of ordered directions

○ **D.** a "Problem and Solution" text, presenting a problem and then showing a solution or group of solutions

Part B

Which detail from the passage best supports your answer to Part A?

○ **A.** The fact that most of the reindeer died is a problem.

○ **B.** The passage describes how the reindeers' weights changed over time.

○ **C.** The passage narrows down reasons as to why the reindeer died.

○ **D.** The passage describes healthy reindeer and sick reindeer.

COMMON CORE STATE STANDARDS

Informational Text 1. Quote accurately from a text when explaining what the text says explicitly and when drawing inferences from the text. **Informational Text 5.** Compare and contrast the overall structure (e.g., chronology, comparison, cause/effect, problem/solution) of events, ideas, concepts, or information in two or more texts.

Next

Vocabulary

Directions: Read the questions below and choose the best answer.

4. **Part A**

   Based on context clues, what does the word "overgrazed" in the sixth paragraph mean?

   ○ **A.** watered so much that the plants became very green

   ○ **B.** grown so slowly that the plants took years to have flowers

   ○ **C.** grown so quickly that the plants were too tall for their roots

   ○ **D.** eaten so much that the plants were destroyed

   Part B

   Which context clue helped you answer Part A?

   ○ **A.** "clipped back"

   ○ **B.** "during winter"

   ○ **C.** "snow-free"

   ○ **D.** "food plants"

COMMON CORE STATE STANDARDS

Informational Text 4. Determine the meaning of general academic and domain-specific words and phrases in a text relevant to a *grade 5 topic or subject area.* **Language 4.** Determine or clarify the meaning of unknown and multiple-meaning words and phrases based on *grade 5 reading and content,* choosing flexibly from a range of strategies. **Language 4.a.** Use context (e.g., cause/effect relationships and comparisons in text) as a clue to the meaning of a word or phrase.

Next

Name _____

5. Part A

If the reindeer starved, evidence would show in their bone marrow. Which word or phrase is a synonym for the word "starved" in the fifth paragraph of the passage?

○ **A.** "well-fed animal"

○ **B.** "cracked"

○ **C.** "had run out of food"

○ **D.** "gone"

Part B

Which sentence about bone marrow best helped you choose the synonym in Part A?

○ **A.** "Knowing this, Klein cracked open the leg bones of the skeletons to examine the marrow."

○ **B.** "None of the animals had fat in their bone marrow when they died."

○ **C.** "This fatty marrow remains in the bones for five years or more after an animal dies."

○ **D.** "An important clue lay hidden in the bones."

COMMON CORE STATE STANDARDS

Informational Text 4. Determine the meaning of general academic and domain-specific words and phrases in a text relevant to a *grade 5 topic or subject area.* **Language 4.** Determine or clarify the meaning of unknown and multiple-meaning words and phrases based on *grade 5 reading and content,* choosing flexibly from a range of strategies. **Language 5.c.** Use the relationship between particular words (e.g., synonyms, antonyms, homographs) to better understand each of the words.

Next

6. **Part A**

The Greek word "artikos" means "of the Bear," or "from the region of the northern constellation of the Bear." Use this meaning to figure out the meaning of the word "arctic" in the fourth paragraph.

○ **A.** a wooded region where bears live

○ **B.** in space where constellations are found

○ **C.** the north pole or near the north pole

○ **D.** the south pole or near the south pole

Part B

Which detail from the passage also helped you figure out the meaning of the word?

○ **A.** "Weather seemed likely to be involved."

○ **B.** "should not have caused such a massive die-off."

○ **C.** "deepest snows and the coldest temperatures . . . in the Bering Sea area."

○ **D.** "As long as they have enough food, . . . reindeer should be able to survive,"

COMMON CORE STATE STANDARDS

Informational Text 4. Determine the meaning of general academic and domain-specific words and phrases in a text relevant to a *grade 5 topic or subject area*. **Language 4.** Determine or clarify the meaning of unknown and multiple-meaning words and phrases based on *grade 5 reading and content,* choosing flexibly from a range of strategies. **Language 4.b.** Use common, grade-appropriate Greek and Latin affixes and roots as clues to the meaning of a word (e.g., *photograph, photosynthesis*).

Next

Writing – Constructed Response

Based on the information in the passage from the selection *The Mystery of Saint Matthew Island,* write an interview for a children's nature magazine. Think of three questions you would ask the author of this passage. Give answers that the author might say.

Organize the interview questions so the events are in a clear sequence. Use dialogue, description, and sensory details to show the responses of the author to situations and to develop and convey any experiences. Expand on the text by adding your own ideas.

_____

_____

_____

_____

_____

_____

_____

_____

_____

_____

_____

_____

To the Teacher: Use the Writing Rubric on page T17 to assess students' writing.

COMMON CORE STATE STANDARDS

Informational Text 1. Quote accurately from a text when explaining what the text says explicitly and when drawing inferences from the text. **Writing 3.** Write narratives to develop real or imagined experiences or events using effective technique, descriptive details, and clear event sequences. **Writing 3.a.** Orient the reader by establishing a situation and introducing a narrator and/or characters; organize an event sequence that unfolds naturally. **Writing 3.b.** Use narrative techniques, such as dialogue, description, and pacing, to develop experiences and events or show the responses of characters to situations. **Writing 3.d.** Use concrete words and phrases and sensory details to convey experiences and events precisely. **Writing 4.** Produce clear and coherent writing in which the development and organization are appropriate to task, purpose, and audience. **Writing 9.** Draw evidence from literary or informational texts to support analysis, reflection, and research.

Next

Writing – Extended Response

You have read two texts about how animals interact with an environment outside of their natural habitat.

- *The Mystery of Saint Matthew Island*
- *The Truth About Austin's Amazing Bats*

Both the reindeer of Saint Matthew Island and the bats of Austin, Texas, lived outside of their natural habitat, with very different results. Do you think it is a good thing when animals make their homes away from the type of area where they usually live? Why? Write an opinion piece in which you answer these questions. State your opinion and offer reasons supported by details from the selections and your own ideas. Provide a concluding sentence that restates your opinion. Remember to follow the conventions of standard English grammar, capitalization, punctuation, and spelling.

To the Teacher: Tell students they may use the space on this page to plan their writing. Then have them write their response on the following pages. Use the Writing Rubric on page T18 to assess students' writing.

COMMON CORE STATE STANDARDS

Informational Text 1. Quote accurately from a text when explaining what the text says explicitly and when drawing inferences from the text. **Writing 1.** Write opinion pieces on topics or texts, supporting a point of view with reasons and information. **Writing 1.a.** Introduce a topic or text clearly, state an opinion, and create an organizational structure in which ideas are logically grouped to support the writer's purpose. **Writing 1.b.** Provide logically ordered reasons that are supported by facts and details. **Writing 1.d.** Provide a concluding statement or section related to the opinion presented. **Writing 4.** Produce clear and coherent writing in which the development and organization are appropriate to task, purpose, and audience. **Writing 9.** Draw evidence from literary or informational texts to support analysis, reflection, and research. **Language 1.** Demonstrate command of the conventions of standard English grammar and usage when writing or speaking. **Language 2.** Demonstrate command of the conventions of standard English capitalization, punctuation, and spelling when writing.

Next

Name _____

_____

_____

_____

_____

_____

_____

_____

_____

_____

_____

_____

_____

_____

_____

_____

_____

_____

_____

Next

_____

_____

_____

_____

_____

_____

_____

_____

_____

_____

_____

_____

_____

_____

_____

_____

_____

_____

_____

_____

_____

_____

Name _____

Directions: Read the following passage. Use information from the passage to answer the questions.

King Midas and the Golden Touch

as told by Charlotte Craft

The stranger's smile broadened. "Well, then, what would make you a happier man?"

Midas thought for only a moment. "Perhaps if everything I touched would turn to gold," he said.

"That is your wish?"

"Yes, for then it would always be at my fingertips," Midas assured him.

"Think carefully, my friend," cautioned the visitor.

"Yes," replied Midas. "The golden touch would bring me all the happiness I need."

"And so it shall be yours."

With that, the mysterious figure became brighter and brighter, until the light became so intense that Midas had to close his eyes. When he opened them, he was alone once again.

Had the enchantment worked?

Midas eagerly rubbed the great brass door key but was greatly disappointed. There was no gold in his hands. Bewildered, he looked around the dim room and wondered if perhaps he had been dreaming.

But when King Midas awoke the next day, he found his bedchamber bathed in golden light. Glistening in the morning sun, the plain linen bedcovers had been transformed into finely spun gold!

Jumping out of bed, he gasped with astonishment. The bedpost turned to gold as soon as he touched it. "It's true," he cried. "I have the golden touch!"

Midas pulled on his clothes. He was thrilled to find himself wearing a handsome suit of gold—never mind that it was a bit heavy. He slid his spectacles onto his nose. To his delight, they too turned to gold—never mind that he couldn't see through them. With a gift as great as this, he thought, no inconvenience could be too great.

Without wasting another moment, Midas rushed out of the room, through the palace, and into the garden.

Next

The roses glistened with the morning dew, and their scent gently perfumed the air. Midas went from bush to bush, touching each of the blossoms.

"How happy Aurelia will be when she sees these roses of gold!" he exclaimed. He never noticed how the perfect golden blossoms drooped and pulled down the bushes with their weight.

Soon it was time for breakfast. Midas sat down just as Aurelia entered the room, clutching a golden rose, her face wet with tears.

"Father, Father, a horrible thing has happened," she said, sobbing. "I went to the garden to pick you a flower, but all of the roses have become hard and yellow."

"They are golden roses now, my love, and will never fade."

"But I miss their scent, Father," cried Aurelia.

"I am sorry, my dear. I thought only to please you. Now we can buy all the roses you could ever wish for." Midas smiled at his daughter to comfort her. "Please wipe your eyes, and we'll have our breakfast together."

Midas lifted a spoonful of porridge to his mouth, but as soon as the porridge touched his lips it turned into a hard golden lump.

Perhaps if I eat quickly, he thought, puzzled, and snatched a fig from a bowl of fruit. It turned to solid gold before he could take a bite. He reached out for some bread, but his fingertips had no sooner brushed against the loaf than it, too, turned to gold. He tried cheese and even a spoonful of jam, but all to no avail. "How am I to eat?" he grumbled.

"What's wrong, Father?" asked Aurelia.

"Nothing," he answered, wishing not to worry her. "Nothing at all, my child."

But Midas began to wring his hands. If he was hungry now, he imagined how much more hungry he would be by dinner.

And then he began to wonder: Will I ever eat again?

Text-Based Comprehension

Directions: Read the questions below and choose the best answer.

1. **Part A**

   Which words best compare and contrast Midas's feelings about his golden touch at the beginning and at the end of this passage?

   ○ **A.** at the beginning, calm; at the end, enthusiastic
   ○ **B.** at the beginning, disappointed; at the end, happy
   ○ **C.** at the beginning, thrilled; at the end, unsure
   ○ **D.** at the beginning, cautious; at the end, depressed

   Part B

   Which detail from the passage helps support these word choices?

   ○ **A.** "When he opened them, he was alone once again." . . . "he gasped with astonishment."
   ○ **B.** "Bewildered, he . . . wondered if perhaps he had been dreaming." . . . "'I have the golden touch!'"
   ○ **C.** "Midas rushed out of the room, . . . and into the garden." . . . "'I am sorry, my dear. I thought only to please you.'"
   ○ **D.** "To his delight, they too turned to gold" . . . "he began to wonder: Will I ever eat again?"

COMMON CORE STATE STANDARDS

Literature 1. Quote accurately from a text when explaining what the text says explicitly and when drawing inferences from the text. **Literature 2.** Determine a theme of a story, drama, or poem from details in the text, including how characters in a story or drama respond to challenges or how the speaker in a poem reflects upon a topic; summarize the text. **Literature 3.** Compare and contrast two or more characters, settings, or events in a story or drama, drawing on specific details in the text (e.g., how characters interact).

2. **Part A**

What is a main theme of this passage?

○ **A.** You cannot be too rich.

○ **B.** Gold is better than gems.

○ **C.** Always be brave.

○ **D.** Be careful what you wish for.

Part B

Which sentence from the passage best supports this theme?

○ **A.** "'Think carefully, my friend,'"

○ **B.** "With a gift as great as this,"

○ **C.** "Had the enchantment worked?"

○ **D.** "'I have the golden touch!'"

COMMON CORE STATE STANDARDS

Literature 1. Quote accurately from a text when explaining what the text says explicitly and when drawing inferences from the text. **Literature 2.** Determine a theme of a story, drama, or poem from details in the text, including how characters in a story or drama respond to challenges or how the speaker in a poem reflects upon a topic; summarize the text.

Next

3. **Part A**

When Midas and Aurelia talk about the golden roses, which phrase is an opinion?

○ **A.** "her face wet with tears."

○ **B.** "'a horrible thing has happened,'"

○ **C.** "'golden roses . . . will never fade.'"

○ **D.** "'But I miss their scent, Father,'"

Part B

Which detail from the passage helped you identify it as an opinion?

○ **A.** Aurelia is a young girl; Midas is an adult man.

○ **B.** Midas likes the golden roses; Aurelia is upset about them.

○ **C.** Aurelia has just entered the room.

○ **D.** Midas wants to comfort Aurelia.

COMMON CORE STATE STANDARDS

Literature 1. Quote accurately from a text when explaining what the text says explicitly and when drawing inferences from the text.

Next

Vocabulary

Directions: Read the questions below and choose the best answer.

4. **Part A**

One meaning of the suffix "-ful" is "full of." Use this meaning to figure out the meaning of the word "spoonful" in the passage.

- ○ **A.** the entire amount held by a spoon
- ○ **B.** the use of a spoon at a table
- ○ **C.** a teaspoon
- ○ **D.** a tablespoon

Part B

Which detail from the passage also helped you figure out the meaning of the word?

- ○ **A.** Midas is very rich.
- ○ **B.** Midas is trying to eat.
- ○ **C.** A palace would have many types of spoons.
- ○ **D.** A spoon made of gold would be very strong.

COMMON CORE STATE STANDARDS

Literature 4. Determine the meaning of words and phrases as they are used in a text, including figurative language such as metaphors and similes. **Foundational Skills 3.a.** Use combined knowledge of all letter-sound correspondences, syllabication patterns, and morphology (e.g., roots and affixes) to read accurately unfamiliar multisyllabic words in context and out of context.

Next

5. **Part A**

The passage contains the sentence: "He reached out for some bread, but his fingertips had no sooner brushed against the loaf than it, too, turned to gold." Which meaning of the word "brushed" is used in the sentence?

○ **A.** metal with a smooth, dull surface

○ **B.** fabric with a type of soft surface

○ **C.** lightly passed across

○ **D.** groomed with a hair tool

Part B

Which detail from the passage best helped you answer Part A?

○ **A.** Midas turns things to gold when he touches them.

○ **B.** Midas lives in a palace with a fancy bedchamber.

○ **C.** Midas is using silverware to eat breakfast.

○ **D.** Midas likes to be surrounded by beautiful riches.

COMMON CORE STATE STANDARDS

Literature 4. Determine the meaning of words and phrases as they are used in a text, including figurative language such as metaphors and similes. **Language 4.** Determine or clarify the meaning of unknown and multiple-meaning words and phrases based on *grade 5 reading and content,* choosing flexibly from a range of strategies. **Language 4.a.** Use context (e.g., cause/effect relationships and comparisons in text) as a clue to the meaning of a word or phrase.

Next

6. **Part A**

The passage contains a paragraph with the sentence: "Midas eagerly rubbed the great brass door key but was greatly disappointed." Which word is an antonym for the root word "eager"?

- ○ **A.** the root word "rub"
- ○ **B.** the root word "disappoint"
- ○ **C.** the word "great"
- ○ **D.** the word "key"

Part B

Which word from that paragraph helped you choose the antonym in Part A?

- ○ **A.** "perhaps"
- ○ **B.** "dim"
- ○ **C.** "Bewildered,"
- ○ **D.** "but"

COMMON CORE STATE STANDARDS

Literature 4. Determine the meaning of words and phrases as they are used in a text, including figurative language such as metaphors and similes. **Language 4.** Determine or clarify the meaning of unknown and multiple-meaning words and phrases based on *grade 5 reading and content,* choosing flexibly from a range of strategies. **Language 5.c.** Use the relationship between particular words (e.g., synonyms, antonyms, homographs) to better understand each of the words.

Next

Writing – Constructed Response

Based on the information in the passage from the selection *King Midas and the Golden Touch,* write a paragraph that tells whether you agree or disagree with this statement: "Happiness cannot be bought."

State your opinion and support it with reasons. Use your own ideas as well as details from the text. Conclude with a sentence that restates your opinion.

_____

_____

_____

_____

_____

_____

_____

_____

_____

_____

_____

_____

_____

To the Teacher: Use the Writing Rubric on page T17 to assess students' writing.

COMMON CORE STATE STANDARDS

Literature 1. Quote accurately from a text when explaining what the text says explicitly and when drawing inferences from the text. **Writing 1.** Write opinion pieces on topics or texts, supporting a point of view with reasons and information. **Writing 1.a.** Introduce a topic or text clearly, state an opinion, and create an organizational structure in which ideas are logically grouped to support the writer's purpose. **Writing 1.b.** Provide logically ordered reasons that are supported by facts and details. **Writing 1.d.** Provide a concluding statement or section related to the opinion presented. **Writing 4.** Produce clear and coherent writing in which the development and organization are appropriate to task, purpose, and audience. **Writing 9.** Draw evidence from literary or informational texts to support analysis, reflection, and research.

Next

Writing – Extended Response

You have read two texts about topics that are first viewed in a different way.

- *King Midas and the Golden Touch*
- *The Truth About Austin's Amazing Bats*

Compare and contrast King Midas's view of unlimited gold in *King Midas and the Golden Touch* and the people in Austin, Texas, and their feelings towards the city's bats in *The Truth About Austin's Amazing Bats*. Write an essay in which you tell how the characters' views of these topics change over time. Introduce the topic and provide a general observation and focus. Develop your essay with facts, details, and examples from the selections. Provide a concluding statement that sums up your main points. Remember to follow the conventions of standard English grammar, capitalization, punctuation, and spelling.

To the Teacher: Tell students they may use the space on this page to plan their writing. Then have them write their response on the following pages. Use the Writing Rubric on page T18 to assess students' writing.

COMMON CORE STATE STANDARDS

Informational Text 1. Quote accurately from a text when explaining what the text says explicitly and when drawing inferences from the text. **Writing 2.** Write informative/explanatory texts to examine a topic and convey ideas and information clearly. **Writing 2.a.** Introduce a topic clearly, provide a general observation and focus, and group related information logically; include formatting (e.g., headings), illustrations, and multimedia when useful to aiding comprehension. **Writing 2.b.** Develop the topic with facts, definitions, concrete details, quotations, or other information and examples related to the topic. **Writing 2.e.** Provide a concluding statement or section related to the information or explanation presented. **Writing 4.** Produce clear and coherent writing in which the development and organization are appropriate to task, purpose, and audience. **Writing 9.** Draw evidence from literary or informational texts to support analysis, reflection, and research. **Language 1.** Demonstrate command of the conventions of standard English grammar and usage when writing or speaking. **Language 2.** Demonstrate command of the conventions of standard English capitalization, punctuation, and spelling when writing.

Name _____

_____

_____

_____

_____

_____

_____

_____

_____

_____

_____

_____

_____

_____

_____

_____

_____

_____

Next

_____

_____

_____

_____

_____

_____

_____

_____

_____

_____

_____

_____

_____

_____

_____

_____

_____

_____

Name _____

Directions: Read the following passage. Use information from the passage to answer the questions.

The *Hindenburg*
by Patrick O'Brien

In Germany in 1900, the first dirigible was successfully flown. This mammoth airship consisted of several giant, gas-filled balloons inside a hard, hollow structure that was moved along by motors and steered by fins. In 1931 the most advanced dirigible yet, the Graf Zeppelin, *began flying from Germany across the Atlantic and back, carrying twenty passengers in dreamy luxury. Meanwhile, its designer, Hugo Eckener, had even grander plans in mind. . . .*

On May 3, 1937, sixty-one crew members and thirty-six passengers boarded the *Hindenburg* for the flight to America. Fourteen-year-old Werner Franz was thrilled to be a cabin boy on the famous airship. He was the youngest member of the crew. Two of the passengers were even younger—Werner and Wallace Doehner, ages six and eight. Somewhere over the Atlantic, a steward politely took away Werner's toy truck. It made sparks when it rolled. In an airship filled with explosive hydrogen, sparks could mean disaster.

The *Hindenburg* cruised low over the icebergs of the North Atlantic, close to the spot where the *Titanic* had gone down twenty-five years before. At four o'clock on the afternoon of May 6, the *Hindenburg* arrived over the landing field in Lakehurst, New Jersey.

There were thunderstorms in the area, so it cruised south over the beaches of the Atlantic coast to wait out the storms. Shortly after seven o'clock, the *Hindenburg* returned to the landing field and slowed to a stop about 250 feet above the ground. The crew dropped ropes from the ship's nose so the men below could help bring the ship in. Everything was done according to plan. It was a routine landing. There was no warning of what was about to happen.

In thirty-two seconds, the mighty airship *Hindenburg* was a mass of flaming wreckage on the ground.

Amazingly, of the ninety-seven people on board, sixty-seven survived the explosion. One person on the ground was killed, and five survivors died later in the hospital.

Next

One passenger who was an acrobat was able to hang on outside a window of the burning airship until it was low enough that he could drop off onto the sandy ground below. He stood up, brushed himself off, and limped away. One older couple walked down the steps of the slowly falling ship as if it was a normal landing. They escaped, injured but alive. The Doehner brothers survived when their mother threw them out of a window into the arms of the rescuers below.

Werner Franz, the fourteen-year-old cabin boy, rode the flaming airship almost all the way to the ground. A large water tank in the ship above his head burst, drenching him with water. He jumped to the ground as the flaming airship was falling around him and dashed out, soaking wet but unharmed.

The cause of the *Hindenburg* explosion is still a mystery. Hugo Eckener felt that there was static electricity in the air because of the thunderstorms in the area, and that this electricity might have ignited some hydrogen that was leaking near the back of the airship. Some people believe, however, that a bomb caused the explosion. There was no evidence of a bomb, but the swastikas on the tail of the ship might have made the *Hindenburg* a target for people who wanted to destroy a symbol of Nazi power.

Millions of people around the world watched newsreels of the *Hindenburg* explosion and heard reports about it on the radio. Zeppelins were now seen as death traps, and all interest in building more of them died with the *Hindenburg*. Eckener wrote that "it appeared to me the hopeless end of a great dream, a kind of end of the world."

Next

Text-Based Comprehension

Directions: Read the questions below and choose the best answer.

1. **Part A**

   Which detail in the last paragraph is an opinion?

   ○ A. "'the hopeless end of a great dream,'"

   ○ B. "Millions of people around the world watched"

   ○ C. "interest in building more of them died"

   ○ D. "Zeppelins were now seen as death traps,"

   Part B

   Which words helped you identify it as an opinion?

   ○ A. "me," "hopeless"

   ○ B. "Millions," "newsreels"

   ○ C. "seen," "death traps"

   ○ D. "explosion," "end of the world"

COMMON CORE STATE STANDARDS

Informational Text 1. Quote accurately from a text when explaining what the text says explicitly and when drawing inferences from the text.

Next

2. **Part A**

What is the unstated main idea of the next-to-last paragraph?

○ **A.** It was dangerous for a zeppelin to be in a thunderstorm.

○ **B.** The Nazis and their power were hated in 1937.

○ **C.** No one knows exactly why the *Hindenburg* caught fire.

○ **D.** Filling zeppelins with hydrogen was a mistake.

Part B

Which sentence from the paragraph best supports this main idea?

○ **A.** "might have ignited some hydrogen that was leaking"

○ **B.** "The cause of the *Hindenburg* explosion is still a mystery."

○ **C.** "there was static electricity in the air because of the thunderstorms"

○ **D.** "the swastikas . . . might have made the *Hindenburg* a target"

COMMON CORE STATE STANDARDS

Informational Text 1. Quote accurately from a text when explaining what the text says explicitly and when drawing inferences from the text. **Informational Text 2.** Determine two or more main ideas of a text and explain how they are supported by key details; summarize the text.

Next

3. **Part A**

Which of these events happens last?

○ **A.** The *Hindenburg* cruises over coastal beaches.

○ **B.** The *Hindenburg* comes to a stop in Lakehurst.

○ **C.** The *Hindenburg* crosses the Atlantic Ocean.

○ **D.** The *Hindenburg* is boarded by ninety-seven people.

Part B

Which phrase best helped you sequence the events in Part A?

○ **A.** "On May 3, 1937,"

○ **B.** "on the afternoon of May 6,"

○ **C.** "In thirty-two seconds,"

○ **D.** "Shortly after seven o'clock,"

COMMON CORE STATE STANDARDS

Informational Text 1. Quote accurately from a text when explaining what the text says explicitly and when drawing inferences from the text. **Informational Text 3.** Explain the relationships or interactions between two or more individuals, events, ideas, or concepts in a historical, scientific, or technical text based on specific information in the text.

Next

Vocabulary

Directions: Read the questions below and choose the best answer.

4. **Part A**

   Based on context clues, what is the best definition of the word "routine" in the third paragraph of the passage?

   ○ **A.** unusual
   ○ **B.** tricky
   ○ **C.** normal
   ○ **D.** scary

   Part B

   Which context clue from the passage best helped you answer Part A?

   ○ **A.** "Everything was done according to plan."
   ○ **B.** "returned to the landing field and slowed to a stop"
   ○ **C.** "it cruised south over the beaches of the Atlantic coast"
   ○ **D.** "The crew dropped ropes from the ship's nose"

COMMON CORE STATE STANDARDS

Informational Text 4. Determine the meaning of general academic and domain-specific words and phrases in a text relevant to a *grade 5 topic or subject area.* **Language 4.** Determine or clarify the meaning of unknown and multiple-meaning words and phrases based on *grade 5 reading and content,* choosing flexibly from a range of strategies. **Language 4.a.** Use context (e.g., cause/effect relationships and comparisons in text) as a clue to the meaning of a word or phrase.

Next

5. **Part A**

Which meaning of the word "field" is used in the second paragraph?

○ **A.** a small part of a general subject

○ **B.** the place where a war is fought

○ **C.** a part of a flag

○ **D.** an open, flat area

Part B

Which word or phrase in the paragraph is the best clue to the meaning of the word?

○ **A.** "four o'clock"

○ **B.** *"Hindenburg"*

○ **C.** "landing"

○ **D.** "Lakehurst, New Jersey"

COMMON CORE STATE STANDARDS

Informational Text 4. Determine the meaning of general academic and domain-specific words and phrases in a text relevant to a *grade 5 topic or subject area.* **Language 4.** Determine or clarify the meaning of unknown and multiple-meaning words and phrases based on *grade 5 reading and content,* choosing flexibly from a range of strategies. **Language 4.a.** Use context (e.g., cause/effect relationships and comparisons in text) as a clue to the meaning of a word or phrase. **Language 5.c.** Use the relationship between particular words (e.g., synonyms, antonyms, homographs) to better understand each of the words.

Next

6. **Part A**

In the paragraph about Werner Franz's escape, which word or phrase is a synonym for the word "drenching" in the last sentence in the passage?

○ **A.** "flaming"

○ **B.** "falling"

○ **C.** "dashed out"

○ **D.** "soaking wet"

Part B

Which detail from the paragraph helped you choose the synonym in Part A?

○ **A.** "A large water tank . . . burst,"

○ **B.** "rode . . . almost all the way to the ground."

○ **C.** "He jumped to the ground"

○ **D.** "fourteen-year-old cabin boy,"

COMMON CORE STATE STANDARDS

Informational Text 4. Determine the meaning of general academic and domain-specific words and phrases in a text relevant to a *grade 5 topic or subject area.* **Language 4.** Determine or clarify the meaning of unknown and multiple-meaning words and phrases based on *grade 5 reading and content,* choosing flexibly from a range of strategies. **Language 5.c.** Use the relationship between particular words (e.g., synonyms, antonyms, homographs) to better understand each of the words.

Next

Writing – Constructed Response

Based on the information in the passage from the selection *The* Hindenburg, write a journal entry for May 6, 1937, the day of the *Hindenburg* disaster. Write the entry from the point of view of Hugo Eckener, the designer of the *Hindenburg*.

Use details from the text to establish the situation. Use description to develop the events, and organize them in a clear sequence. Use sensory details to convey Eckener's experience precisely. Provide a conclusion that sums up the day's events.

_____

_____

_____

_____

_____

_____

_____

_____

_____

_____

_____

_____

_____

To the Teacher: Use the Writing Rubric on page T17 to assess students' writing.

COMMON CORE STATE STANDARDS

Informational Text 1. Quote accurately from a text when explaining what the text says explicitly and when drawing inferences from the text. **Writing 3.** Write narratives to develop real or imagined experiences or events using effective technique, descriptive details, and clear event sequences. **Writing 3.a.** Orient the reader by establishing a situation and introducing a narrator and/or characters; organize an event sequence that unfolds naturally. **Writing 3.b.** Use narrative techniques, such as dialogue, description, and pacing, to develop experiences and events or show the responses of characters to situations. **Writing 3.d.** Use concrete words and phrases and sensory details to convey experiences and events precisely. **Writing 4.** Produce clear and coherent writing in which the development and organization are appropriate to task, purpose, and audience. **Writing 9.** Draw evidence from literary or informational texts to support analysis, reflection, and research.

Next

Writing – Extended Response

You have read two texts that tell about real-life tragedies.

- *The* Hindenburg
- *The Mystery of Saint Matthew Island*

Both of the stories describe real-life tragedies using description and details. Write an essay in which you compare each of the stories' overall structure of events and information. Introduce the topic and then develop it with facts, details, and examples from the selections. Provide a concluding statement that sums up your main points. Remember to follow the conventions of standard English grammar, capitalization, punctuation, and spelling.

To the Teacher: Tell students they may use the space on this page to plan their writing. Then have them write their response on the following pages. Use the Writing Rubric on page T18 to assess students' writing.

COMMON CORE STATE STANDARDS

Informational Text 1. Quote accurately from a text when explaining what the text says explicitly and when drawing inferences from the text. **Writing 2.** Write informative/explanatory texts to examine a topic and convey ideas and information clearly. **Writing 2.a.** Introduce a topic clearly, provide a general observation and focus, and group related information logically; include formatting (e.g., headings), illustrations, and multimedia when useful to aiding comprehension. **Writing 2.b.** Develop the topic with facts, definitions, concrete details, quotations, or other information and examples related to the topic. **Writing 2.e.** Provide a concluding statement or section related to the information or explanation presented. **Writing 4.** Produce clear and coherent writing in which the development and organization are appropriate to task, purpose, and audience. **Writing 9.** Draw evidence from literary or informational texts to support analysis, reflection, and research. **Language 1.** Demonstrate command of the conventions of standard English grammar and usage when writing or speaking. **Language 2.** Demonstrate command of the conventions of standard English capitalization, punctuation, and spelling when writing.

Next

Name _____

_____

_____

_____

_____

_____

_____

_____

_____

_____

_____

_____

_____

_____

_____

_____

_____

_____

_____

Next

_____

_____

_____

_____

_____

_____

_____

_____

_____

_____

_____

_____

_____

_____

_____

_____

_____

_____

Directions: Read the following passage. Use information from the passage to answer the questions.

Sweet Music in Harlem

by Debbie A. Taylor

As C. J. hurried away, he could hear the people in the barbershop buzzing about the photographer. "I've got to find that hat," C. J. muttered to himself.

C. J. rushed around the corner and into the jam-packed Eat and Run Diner. Just inside the door he jumped back as a waitress zipped past, balancing plates of ham and eggs on one arm and home fries and sausage on the other.

The waitress grinned at C. J., her apron still swaying from her dash across the room. "Hey, C. J.," she said.

"Hi, Mattie Dee," said C. J. "Did Uncle Click leave his hat here? A photographer from *Highnote* magazine is coming to take his picture in a few minutes, and Uncle Click needs his hat."

"Honey, Click didn't leave his hat, but he did leave this," said Mattie Dee. She pulled a handkerchief from her pocket and dropped it into C. J.'s hand.

"Your uncle leaves his things all over Harlem, but when he wails on his trumpet, the saltshakers bounce! And if you keep practicing, one day you'll make them bounce too."

"Thanks for the hankie, Mattie Dee," C. J. said.

"Did you say a photographer from *Highnote* is coming?" Mattie Dee asked. "I'd love to be in the picture—especially if I can stand right next to your handsome uncle."

As C. J. left the diner, he could hear Mattie Dee telling her customers about the photographer. "But I've still got to find Uncle Click's hat!" C. J. moaned.

C. J. raced down the block, then bounded down the stairs of the Midnight Melody Club. Even though the club was closed, eight musicians were crowded onto the small stage, playing as if it were still show time. The bass player's eyes glistened as he plucked his instrument. The vibraphone player tapped the keys with his eyes closed.

Next

"C. J.!" the drummer shouted without losing the beat. "We're saving a spot for you here. I reckon you'll be joining us in a few years."

A woman strolled toward C. J. from the back of the club. She didn't seem to notice that it wasn't nighttime. She still wore a fancy dress, and rings glittered on her fingers.

"Miss Alma!" C. J. called. "A photographer from *Highnote* magazine is coming to take Uncle Click's picture, and he can't find his hat. Did he leave it onstage last night?"

Canary Alma shook her head. "Your uncle didn't leave his hat here, but he did leave this," she said, and plucked a bow tie from the piano bench. "He's forgetful, but when Click blows his trumpet the wallpaper curls."

C. J. thanked Canary Alma and slid the tie over his wrist.

"A photographer from *Highnote*!" Canary Alma exclaimed, smoothing her dress. "My face next to your uncle's will give that photo a touch of class."

C. J.'s shoulders drooped as he left the Midnight Melody Club. He didn't want to disappoint Uncle Click, but he just couldn't find that hat anywhere.

C. J. dragged his feet up the steps of the brownstone where his uncle waited. A lump like a sour ball wedged in C. J.'s throat.

"Uncle Click," C. J. said. "I didn't find your hat, but I did find these." He held out the watch, the handkerchief, and the bow tie.

Uncle Click looked at C. J., and a huge smile spread across his face. "Looks like you found something else too," he said, pointing behind C. J.

C. J. turned around. Big Charlie Garlic, Mattie Dee, and Canary Alma were walking down the street toward them. But they weren't alone! They were followed by men from the barbershop, people from the diner, and musicians from the Midnight Melody Club. There were also folks C. J. had never seen before and people he'd only seen on posters or record covers.

"Hey, Click," called Charlie Garlic. "You sure know how to gather a crowd."

Next

Name _____

Text-Based Comprehension

Directions: Read the questions below and choose the best answer.

1. **Part A**

   Which two events at the Midnight Melody Club happen at the same time?

   ○ **A.** C. J. arrives at the club and Uncle Click is playing the trumpet.

   ○ **B.** Eight musicians are playing and the drummer talks with C. J.

   ○ **C.** Canary Alma wears a fancy dress and Uncle Click forgets his hat at the club.

   ○ **D.** Canary Alma gives C. J. the bow tie and the photographer takes the photograph.

   Part B

   Which detail from the passage helped you choose the two events in Part A?

   ○ **A.** "then bounded down the stairs"

   ○ **B.** "C. J. thanked Canary Alma"

   ○ **C.** "without losing the beat."

   ○ **D.** "rings glittered on her fingers."

COMMON CORE STATE STANDARDS

Literature 1. Quote accurately from a text when explaining what the text says explicitly and when drawing inferences from the text. **Literature 3.** Compare and contrast two or more characters, settings, or events in a story or drama, drawing on specific details in the text (e.g., how characters interact).

Next

2. **Part A**

How does C. J. respond to the challenge of finding Uncle Click's hat?

○ **A.** He tells his uncle he will look but plays music with a band instead.

○ **B.** He starts the search but gets distracted by other people.

○ **C.** He gives up very soon and heads for home.

○ **D.** He goes to different places and works hard to find it.

Part B

Which sentence from the passage does **not** support your answer to Part A?

○ **A.** "There were also folks C. J. had never seen before and people he'd only seen on posters or record covers."

○ **B.** "C.J. raced down the block, then bounded down the stairs of the Midnight Melody Club."

○ **C.** "C. J. rushed around the corner and into the jam-packed Eat and Run Diner."

○ **D.** "'But I've still got to find Uncle Click's hat!' C.J. moaned."

COMMON CORE STATE STANDARDS

Literature 1. Quote accurately from a text when explaining what the text says explicitly and when drawing inferences from the text. **Literature 2.** Determine a theme of a story, drama, or poem from details in the text, including how characters in a story or drama respond to challenges or how the speaker in a poem reflects upon a topic; summarize the text.

Next

Name _____

3. Part A

Which sentence from the passage is an opinion?

○ **A.** "A woman strolled toward C. J. from the back of the club."

○ **B.** "'My face next to your uncle's will give that photo a touch of class.'"

○ **C.** "The bass player's eyes glistened as he plucked his instrument."

○ **D.** "'But I've still got to find Uncle Click's hat!' C. J. moaned."

Part B

Which words from the sentence helped you identify it as an opinion?

○ **A.** "got to find," "moaned"

○ **B.** "glistened," "plucked"

○ **C.** "strolled toward," "back of the club"

○ **D.** "give," "touch of class"

COMMON CORE STATE STANDARDS

Literature 1. Quote accurately from a text when explaining what the text says explicitly and when drawing inferences from the text.

Next

Vocabulary

Directions: Read the questions below and choose the best answer.

4. **Part A**

   Which meaning of the homograph "keys" is used in the paragraph where C. J. runs into the Midnight Melody Club?

   ○ **A.** a metal tool for unlocking a lock

   ○ **B.** a part of a musical instrument

   ○ **C.** a guide for symbols on a map

   ○ **D.** something important in a problem's solution

   Part B

   Which detail from the passage best helped you figure out the meaning of the homograph?

   ○ **A.** "eight musicians were . . . playing"

   ○ **B.** "'Thanks for the hankie,'"

   ○ **C.** "C. J. raced down the block,"

   ○ **D.** "Just inside the door"

COMMON CORE STATE STANDARDS

Literature 4. Determine the meaning of words and phrases as they are used in a text, including figurative language such as metaphors and similes. **Language 5.c.** Use the relationship between particular words (e.g., synonyms, antonyms, homographs) to better understand each of the words.

Next

5. **Part A**

Canary Alma uses a simile when talking about Uncle Click: "He's forgetful, but when Click blows his trumpet the wallpaper curls." What does the simile mean?

○ **A.** When Uncle Click plays the trumpet, it becomes very warm inside.

○ **B.** When Uncle Click plays the trumpet, he takes his bow tie off.

○ **C.** When Uncle Click plays the trumpet, it is spectacular.

○ **D.** When Uncle Click wants to play the trumpet, he forgets where it is.

Part B

Which detail helped you figure out the meaning of the simile?

○ **A.** Uncle Click is very forgetful.

○ **B.** Uncle Click is a handsome man.

○ **C.** Uncle Click plays his trumpet all over Harlem.

○ **D.** Uncle Click is a great musician.

COMMON CORE STATE STANDARDS

Literature 4. Determine the meaning of words and phrases as they are used in a text, including figurative language such as metaphors and similes. **Language 5.a.** Interpret figurative language, including similes and metaphors, in context.

Next

6. **Part A**

A photographer, or someone who takes photographs, is mentioned throughout the passage. The word "photograph" comes from the Greek words "photo-," meaning "light," and "graphein," meaning "to write" or "to draw." Which word is a synonym for the word "photograph"?

- ○ **A.** image
- ○ **B.** piano
- ○ **C.** music
- ○ **D.** magazine

Part B

Which detail from the passage is a clue to the answer to Part A?

- ○ **A.** "wails on his trumpet"
- ○ **B.** "next to your handsome uncle"
- ○ **C.** "take his picture"
- ○ **D.** "in a few minutes"

COMMON CORE STATE STANDARDS

Literature 4. Determine the meaning of words and phrases as they are used in a text, including figurative language such as metaphors and similes. **Language 4.a.** Use context (e.g., cause/effect relationships and comparisons in text) as a clue to the meaning of a word or phrase. **Language 4.b.** Use common, grade-appropriate Greek and Latin affixes and roots as clues to the meaning of a word (e.g., *photograph, photosynthesis*). **Language 5.c.** Use the relationship between particular words (e.g., synonyms, antonyms, homographs) to better understand each of the words.

Next

Name _____

Writing – Constructed Response

Based on the information in the passage from the selection *Sweet Music in Harlem,* write a paragraph that tells whether you agree or disagree with this statement: "Everyone needs a hero to look up to." Be sure to consider how C. J. looks up to his Uncle Click and how it affects C. J.'s life, as well as how any hero has affected your life.

State your opinion and support it with reasons. Use your own ideas as well as details from the text. Conclude with a sentence that restates your opinion.

_____

_____

_____

_____

_____

_____

_____

_____

_____

_____

_____

_____

To the Teacher: Use the Writing Rubric on page T17 to assess students' writing.

COMMON CORE STATE STANDARDS

Literature 1. Quote accurately from a text when explaining what the text says explicitly and when drawing inferences from the text. **Writing 1.** Write opinion pieces on topics or texts, supporting a point of view with reasons and information. **Writing 1.a.** Introduce a topic or text clearly, state an opinion, and create an organizational structure in which ideas are logically grouped to support the writer's purpose. **Writing 1.b.** Provide logically ordered reasons that are supported by facts and details. **Writing 1.d.** Provide a concluding statement or section related to the opinion presented. **Writing 4.** Produce clear and coherent writing in which the development and organization are appropriate to task, purpose, and audience. **Writing 9.** Draw evidence from literary or informational texts to support analysis, reflection, and research.

Next

Writing – Extended Response

You have read two texts about people who strive to reach a goal that is important to them.

- *Sweet Music in Harlem*
- *King Midas and the Golden Touch*

Imagine C. J. finds himself in the mythical kingdom of King Midas, where he has a chance meeting with Midas. They begin to talk about their goals: C. J.'s of becoming a musician and Midas's of having a lot of gold. Write the dialogue between C. J. and Midas using facts and details from both texts. Establish the situation and introduce the characters. Use dialogue, description, and sensory details to convey experiences precisely and to show how the characters responded to their experiences. Remember to follow the conventions of standard English grammar, capitalization, punctuation, and spelling.

To the Teacher: Tell students they may use the space on this page to plan their writing. Then have them write their response on the following pages. Use the Writing Rubric on page T18 to assess students' writing.

COMMON CORE STATE STANDARDS

Literature 1. Quote accurately from a text when explaining what the text says explicitly and when drawing inferences from the text. **Writing 3.** Write narratives to develop real or imagined experiences or events using effective technique, descriptive details, and clear event sequences. **Writing 3.a.** Orient the reader by establishing a situation and introducing a narrator and/or characters; organize an event sequence that unfolds naturally. **Writing 3.b.** Use narrative techniques, such as dialogue, description, and pacing, to develop experiences and events or show the responses of characters to situations. **Writing 3.d.** Use concrete words and phrases and sensory details to convey experiences and events precisely. **Writing 4.** Produce clear and coherent writing in which the development and organization are appropriate to task, purpose, and audience. **Writing 9.** Draw evidence from literary or informational texts to support analysis, reflection, and research. **Language 1.** Demonstrate command of the conventions of standard English grammar and usage when writing or speaking. **Language 2.** Demonstrate command of the conventions of standard English capitalization, punctuation, and spelling when writing.

Name _____

_____

_____

_____

_____

_____

_____

_____

_____

_____

_____

_____

_____

_____

_____

_____

_____

_____

_____

_____

Next

_____

_____

_____

_____

_____

_____

_____

_____

_____

_____

_____

_____

_____

_____

_____

_____

_____

_____

_____